Reaching ME in Me
Kundalini Yoga as Taught by Yogi Bhajan®

Compiled and Illustrated by: Harijot Kaur Khalsa

KRI Reviewer: Gurucharan Singh Khalsa

Senior Editors: Gurucharan Singh Khalsa
Shakti Parwha Kaur Khalsa
Pritpal Kaur Khalsa

Original Recordings: Siri Ved Singh Khalsa

Design & Production: Ravitej Khalsa Design Inc.

Yogi Bhajan Photo: Satsimran Kaur

Published by **Kundalini Research Institute**, PO Box 1819, Santa Cruz, NM 87567
ISBN 0-978-0-9720110-0-6

Reaching ME in Me

There is the "me" we know through our habits, our five senses, and through our reactions to our environment. It is where we start our experience on earth, but it is not where we come from. We come from the Infinite and we go to the Infinite. We begin, as we end, in the "ME" within "me." When we reach the ME within me, in our practical experience, everything changes. We are no longer dependent on anyone or anything. We are self-contained and rely only on the Infinite. We stop trying to *reach* the Infinite, because the Infinite now reaches to us. Blessings come, resources come, prosperity comes, and fulfillment comes. We let go, and let God. The Master's touch is in each of these sets. The touch of a Master who has realized the ME within me is the best guide to opening that same place in ourselves. We are blessed in this collection to have the sets exactly as given by Yogi Bhajan. Practice them with regularity, clarity, and devotion so that you can connect with your original Self.

Acknowledgements

The technology of Kundalini Yoga and White Tantric Yoga was brought to the West from India by the grace of Siri Singh Sahib Bhai Sahib Harbhajan Singh Khalsa Yogiji (Yogi Bhajan). The teachings in this manual are entirely his gift. We wish to gratefully acknowledge his gift and the inspiration he offered to us all in manifesting our highest potential. Any errors or omissions in this manual are entirely the fault of the Editors and by no means reflect upon the perfection and comprehensiveness of the teachings.

The yoga sets in this manual are classes taught by Yogi Bhajan and are available on audio, DVD and VHS. Although every effort has been made to communicate the technology of these classes accurately, nothing replaces the experience of doing Kundalini Yoga with the Master, Yogi Bhajan. We suggest that you enhance your yoga experience by collecting DVDs of one or more of your favorite sets from this manual. There is something about doing Kundalini Yoga in the presence of the Master, Yogi Bhajan (even on video) that brings out the best yogi within you. To purchase DVDs and audio cassettes, plus other manuals and books on Kundalini Yoga as taught by Yogi Bhajan© go to The Source; http://thesource.kriteachings.org

INTRODUCTION

For Beginners...

If you are a beginning student of Kundalini Yoga, practicing for less than six months, or if you have been practicing without the aid of a certified 3HO Foundation teacher, please read this introduction before you begin to practice from this instruction manual.

Sadhana Guidelines

This manual has been prepared as a supplement and extension to Kundalini Yoga Sadhana Guidelines, 2nd Edition, in which Yogi Bhajan explains yoga, meditation, and the energy that is Kundalini. Also important for beginners are the descriptions of the basics of Kundalini Yoga: asanas (postures), mudras (hand positions), bandhas (energy locks), and mantras (sound currents) written by Gurucharan Singh Khalsa, Director of Training for the Kundalini Research Institute's Aquarian Trainer Academy.

The Teacher

Kundalini Yoga is a spiritual discipline which cannot be practiced without a teacher. However, it is not necessary for the teacher to be physically present when you practice. To establish a creative link with the Master of Kundalini Yoga, Yogi Bhajan, be sure to tune in to his energy flow using the Adi Mantra, "Ong Namo Guru Dev Namo."

Tuning In

Every Kundalini Yoga session begins with chanting the Adi Mantra: "Ong Namo Guru Dev Namo." By chanting it in proper form and consciousness, the student becomes open to the higher self, the source of all guidance, and accesses the protective link between himself or herself and the divine teacher.

How to recite the Adi Mantra:

Sit in a comfortable cross–legged position with the spine straight. Place the palms of the hands together as if in prayer, with the fingers pointing straight up, and then press the joints of the thumbs into the center of the chest, at the sternum. Inhale deeply. Focus your concentration at the third–eye point. As you exhale, chant the entire mantra in one breath. If your breath is not capable of this, take a quick sip of air through the mouth after "Ong Namo" and then chant the rest of the mantra, extending the sound as long as possible. The sound "Dev" is chanted a minor third higher than the other sounds of the mantra.

Ong---   Na-mo---   Gu-ru Dev---   Namo---

As you chant, vibrate the cranium with the sound to create a mild pressure at the third–eye point. Chant this mantra at least three times before beginning your Kundalini Yoga practice.

Pronunciation

The "O" sound in Ong is long, as in "go" and of short duration. The "ng" sound is long and produces a definite vibration on the roof of the mouth and the cranium. The first part of Namo, is short and rhymes with "hum." The "O", as in "go" is held longer. The first syllable of Guru is pronounced as in the word, "good." The second syllable rhymes with "true." The first syllable is short and the second one long. The word, Dev rhymes with "gave."

Definition

Ong is the infinite creative energy experienced in manifestation and activity. It is a variation of the cosmic syllable "Om" which denotes God in His absolute or unmanifested state. God as Creator is called Ong.

Namo has the same root as the Sanskrit word Namaste which means reverent greetings. Namaste is a common greeting in India, accompanied by the palms pressed together at the chest or forehead. It implies bowing down. Together Ong Namo means "I call on the infinite creative consciousness," and opens you to the universal consciousness that guides all action.

Guru is the embodiment of the wisdom that one is seeking. The Guru is the giver of the technology. Dev means higher, subtle, or divine. It refers to the spiritual realms. Namo, in closing the mantra, reaffirms the humble reverence of the student. Taken together, Guru Dev Namo means, "I call on the divine wisdom," whereby you bow before your higher self to guide you in using the knowledge and energy given by the cosmic self.

Mental Focus

The following pages contain many wonderful techniques. To fully appreciate and receive the benefits of each one you will need mental focus. Unless you are directed to do otherwise, focus your concentration on the brow point, which is located between the eyebrows at the root of the nose. With your eyes closed, mentally locate this point by turning your eyes gently upwards and inwards. Remain aware of your breath, your body posture, your movements, and any mantra you may be using, even as you center your awareness at the third eye point.

Linking the Breath With a Mantra

A mantra is a sequence of sounds designed to direct the mind by their rhythmic repetition. To fully utilize the power of mantra, link the mantra with your breath cycle. A common mantra is "Sat Nam" (rhymes with "But Mom"). Sat Nam means "Truth is my identity." Mentally repeat "Sat" as you inhale, and "Nam" as you exhale. In this way you filter your thoughts so that each thought has a positive resolution. Mantra makes it easier to keep up during strenuous exercises and adds depth to the performance of even the simplest ones.

Pacing Yourself

Kundalini yoga exercises may involve rhythmic movement between two or more postures. Begin slowly, keeping a steady rhythm. Increase gradually, being careful not to strain. Usually the more you practice an exercise, the faster you can go. Just be sure that the spine has become warm and flexible before attempting rapid movements. It is important to be aware of your body and to be responsible for its well-being.

IV

Concluding an Exercise

Unless otherwise stated, an exercise is concluded by inhaling and holding the breath briefly. While the breath is being held, apply the mulbandha or root lock, contracting the muscles around the sphincter, the sex organs, and the navel point. Then exhale and relax. This consolidates the effects of any exercise and circulates the energy to your higher centers. Do not hold the breath to the point of dizziness. If you start to feel dizzy or faint, immediately exhale and relax.

Relaxation Between Exercises

An important part of any exercise is the relaxation following it. Unless otherwise specified, you should allow one to three minutes of relaxation in Easy Pose or lying on the back in Corpse Pose after each exercise. The less experienced you are or the more strenuous the exercise, the longer the relaxation period should be. Some sets end with a period of "deep relaxation" which may extend from three to eleven minutes.

Music

Because of the emphasis on the integration of exercise, meditation, and rhythm in Kundalini Yoga, you will find specific music and mantra tapes used during the exercises. We recommend using the same tapes when you practice because they were chosen by Yogi Bhajan with precise effects in mind. If you don't have the specific tape used in a set, you may do the set without music or substitute other meditative music.

The Fingers

In the Yogic tradition each of the fingers relates to a different planetary energy. Through the positioning of these fingers in mudras one can either draw a specific energy into the body, project it out from the body, or combine it with the energies of other fingers to create a desired effect. The little finger is the Mercury finger and it channels communication. The ring finger is the Sun finger and it channels physical vitality. The middle finger is the Saturn finger and it channels emotion. The index finger is the Jupiter finger and it channels wisdom. The thumb represents one's ego or id.

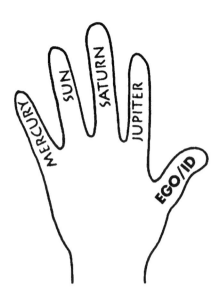

On Your Way...

The exercises in this manual are designed to be safe for most people, provided the instructions are followed carefully. The benefits attributed to these exercises come from centuries-old yogic tradition. Results will vary due to physical differences and the correctness and frequency of practice. The publishers and authors disclaim all liability in connection with the use of the information in individual cases. As with all unsupervised exercise programs, your use of the instructions in this manual is taken at your own risk. If you have any doubts as to the suitability of the exercises, please consult a doctor.

We invite you to now enjoy the practice of the Kundalini Yoga techniques contained in the following pages. If you have any questions or concerns about your practice of Kundalini Yoga, please contact your local KRI Certified teacher.

"It is not that you have to find God.
It's very astonishing to me when people say
'I am doing this to find God'...God has not to be found.
God has not gone on holiday. *You* have to find consciousness.
When you can eliminate your ego and find consciousness,
you can find God in you."

Yogi Bhajan

Table of Contents

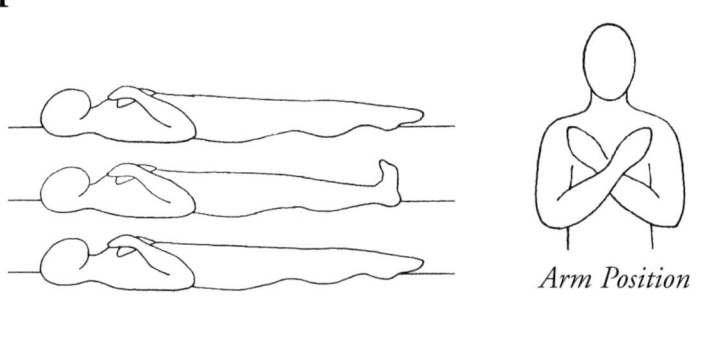

Arm Position

2

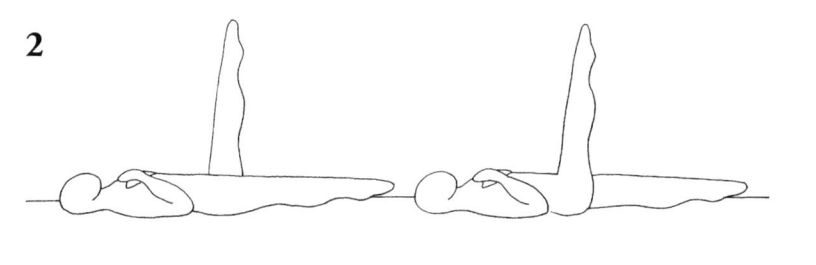

3

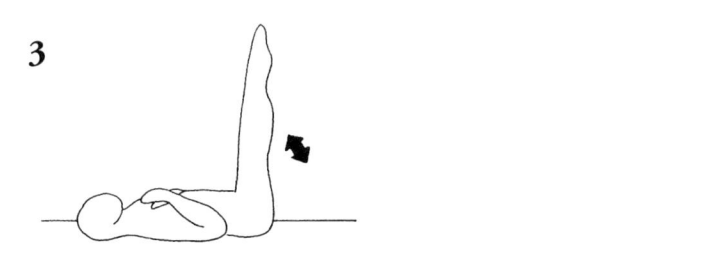

4

Top View

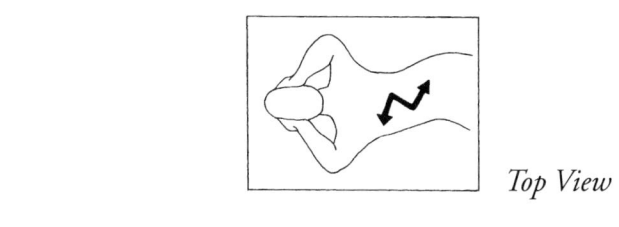

Side View

Adjusting the Centers of Interconnection and Intercommunication

June 24, 1984

1. Lie flat on your back with your feet and legs together, crossing your wrists over your chest like a mummy. Completely relax for 1 Minute. Stay in the position, keep relaxed, and begin pointing and flexing both feet at the same time. Coordinate breath and movement. Move quickly. The breath should be heavy and loud. (If your feet and breath are not moving together, then your temples are out of position.) 4 1/2 Minutes. If you feel pressure at the temples while you are doing this exercise, then slow down the movement.

2. Stay in the same mummy-like position, begin alternate leg lifts to 90 degrees. Keep your legs straight with the toes pointed. Inhale up and exhale down with a loud and powerful breath. Apply upward pressure as you raise each leg. Do not apply pressure as the feet go back to the floor. Feet should silently return to the floor. 3 Minutes.

3. Still in the same mummy-like position, raise both legs to 90 degrees and lower them together. Inhale up and exhale down, moving quickly for 1 Minute. Then continue by doing 52 more leg lifts.

4. Still lying on your back, heavily lock your palms over your ears and temples. Your elbows point upward. Begin moving your pelvic bone and rib cage from side to side like a wriggling fish. Make this diagonal movement so heavy that you can feel it in your temples. Move the pelvic bone, rib cage, and spine. The whole torso moves. If you move heavily and fast, it will take away the age imbalances. 3 1/2 Minutes.
If you cannot copy the fish, how can you copy God. Make the effort. Once you get into the proper movement, you can continue it.

"We are adjusting the two areas that we call the temples. These areas are more important than we know. In the ancient wisdom, they are known as the main centers of each zone of interconnection and intercommunication."

YB

Hand Position when touching shoulder

5. Sit on your heels, stretch your tongue out of your mouth and begin a panting Dog Breath through your mouth, feeling the air striking the back of your throat. 1 Minute. This will give you the energy to do the next exercise.

6. Sit on your heels, arms extended straight out with the palms facing each other. Alternately move each arm up to 45 degrees and back to the center. The left arm moves diagonally up to the right side and returns. Then the right arm moves up to the left and returns. You are drawing a big "X" in the air in front of your body. The movement is fast and powerful. The body will subtly move as the arms move. Cut the heavens. You will feel the movement in the temples and the toes if you really do it strongly. 2 1/2 Minutes.

7. Sitting on your heels with your arms by your sides with the palms facing forward. Bring your hands to your shoulders as if you are pouring water on them. Bring all five fingertips together when they touch the shoulders. 1 1/2 Minutes.
This exercise will make you feel good for the whole day.

8. Still on your heels, begin flexing the whole body. Flex it well, lower back, middle back, upper back, and neck.
1/2 Minute.

9. Sit like a yogi and chant "Hari Har, Hari Har, Hari Har, Haree" in a monotone using the tip of the tongue.
One recitation of the mantra takes about 3 seconds.
Continue for 9 1/2 Minutes.

In class Yogi Bhajan played the gong during the meditation.

To finish: Inhale, hold the breath for 45 seconds, and exhale. Repeat this sequence two more times, each time holding the breath as long as is comfortable.

Activate the Navel to Activate Youth

August 26, 1985

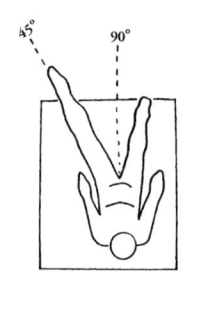

1. Lie down on your back with your arms by your sides and both legs stretched out straight. Raise your left leg out at a forty-five degree angle to the side (See diagram), lifting it up to sixty degrees. Then lower it and continue to rapidly raise and lower the left leg, leaving the right leg stretched out straight on the floor. 2 1/2 Minutes. If you put honest effort into this exercise, it can increase your lung capacity.

1

2. Remain on your back. Begin this variation of alternate leg lifts:
  a. Lift the left leg at a forty-five degree angle to the side (as in exercise one) and lower it.
  b. Raise the right leg straight up and lower it to the floor.
  c. Return to "a" and continue the sequence. 1 1/2 Minutes.

2

3. Still on your back, begin a second variation of alternate leg lifts :

  a. Raise your left leg straight up and lower it.
  b. Raise your left leg out at the forty-five degree angle and lower it.
  c. Raise your right leg straight up and lower it.
  d. Raise your right leg out at the forty-five degree angle and lower it.
  e. Return to "a" and continue the sequence. 2 1/2 Minutes.

3

4. Still lying flat on your back, with your legs together, raise both legs straight up and lower them. Continue raising and lowering both legs together for 1 1/2 Minutes.

4

5. Relax for 1 Minute.

6

6. Lie down flat on your back with your legs stretched out straight on the floor. Raise your torso up to sixty degrees and then lie back down flat. Continue raising and lowering your torso, keeping your legs flat on the floor. 1 1/2 Minutes.

7

7. Lie down flat on your back with your legs stretched out straight on the floor. Raise your torso and your legs up at the same time. (The torso will be angled back at about sixty degrees while the legs will be angled up at about sixty degrees. The body makes a "V" shape. Find your own balance point.) Then lie back flat on the floor. Continue going up and down in this manner. 2 Minutes.

8

8. Lie flat on your back. Raise your torso and your legs at the same time bringing your forehead to your knees. (Both the torso and the legs are off the ground.) Lie back down. Continue this movement for 2 Minutes.
This exercise cleanses the liver.

9

9. Lie down on your stomach, bend your left knee, grab your left ankle with both hands and inhale up into bow pose. Exhale down. Continue the up and down movement. 1 1/2 Minutes. Change legs, grabbing your right ankle and continue the movement. 1 1/2 Minutes.

10

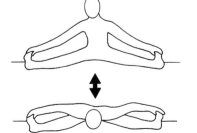

10. Sit up and spread your legs as far apart as you comfortably can. Grab your toes. Inhale sitting up with your spine straight. Exhale and bend your torso forward, bringing your forehead to the floor, if you can. Inhale, rise up, and continue this up and down movement. 1 Minute.

"People will give you everything, if you give yourself discipline."

YB

11

11. Lie down on your back and bring your knees to your chest. Inhale, spread your legs apart, and straighten your knees, extending your legs out to the sides at about 45 degree angle. Exhale, bend your knees, bringing them back down to your chest. Move rapidly. 1 Minute.

12. Still on your back:
   a. Raise both legs straight up.
   b. Spread your legs, extending them out to the sides at a 45 degree angle.
   c. Bend your knees, bringing them back down to your chest.
   d. Extend your legs back out to the sides at a 45 degree angle.
   e. Close your legs, bringing them together so that they point straight up.
   f. Lower both legs to the floor.
   g. Begin the movement again starting at "a".
   Continue the sequence. 2 Minutes.

12

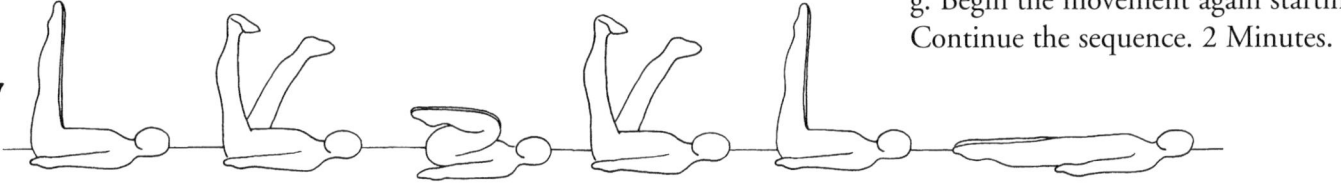

13

13. Sit in Easy Pose. Move your arms quickly and sharply into each of the following positions. Hold the position for 1-2 seconds and then move quickly and sharply into the next position.
   a. Bring your hands in front of your throat with the palms facing each other about 4 inches apart.
   b. Straighten your elbows, opening the arms out to the sides. The arms are up about thirty degrees, palms facing forward and tilting slightly upward.(As if you are offering a hug to the Infinite.)
   c. Bring the arms straight up over the head palms facing each other about 4 inches apart.
   d. Bring the arms back down to position "a" and continue this sequence. 1 Minute.

14. Sit like a yogi in Easy Pose with your hands in Gyan Mudra. Concentrate and meditate to Sangeet Kaur's tape of *Naad, the Blessing.* Breathe long, slow, and deep. Be still as a statue. 22 Minutes.

"This is a powerful set for advanced students. It should be approached gradually and with discipline as you master it." GCSK

1

2

5

1-30-86

1. Stretch your legs straight out in front. Grab your toes and stretch the spine forward. Inhale and tilt the head up, stretching the back of your neck. Exhale and bring your chin to your chest. Maintain the stretch in the spine. Continue to move your head with the breath, being careful not to compress the vertebrae of the neck. Breathe in and out fast and powerfully. 1 1/2 Minutes.

"As a teacher, you must experience everything that you share."

YB

2. Lie down on your back, begin Breath of Fire, and dance your body. Move any way you wish, but don't raise any part of your body off the floor. No part should be stable, all parts should move. It's a physically violent reaction to get rid of internal violence in a controlled fashion. It's "you against you." Take all the pain out, don't hold anything in. 3 1/2 Minutes

3. Relax on your back. Go to sleep. Listen to the tape of the gong meditation played by Yogi Bhajan for this class. Bring your strength to your toes and go with the gong. The three rhythms of the gong will work on the glandular system. If you give yourself a good chance, it will work on the pineal gland.
11 Minutes.
In order to receive the benefits of this set, it is required that you meditate to the gong meditation played by Yogi Bhajan in this class. (See the Introduction for where to purchase this tape.)

4. Move feet and hands, wake yourself up.

5. Sit in Easy Pose. Chant "God and Me, Me and God, Are One" meditatively going from chakra to chakra. 15 Minutes.

6. Inhale, hold your breath 20-30 seconds and stretch your body. Exhale. Inhale and move your body all around, stimulating your energy. 30 Seconds. Exhale and relax.

Balance the Body and Spine

6-13-84
Morning Class

1. Sit in Crow Pose and lock your hands behind your neck. Inhale and stand up. Exhale and squat back down in Crow Pose. Try to build the arch in your foot, don't allow it to flatten with the movement. 6 Minutes. (Do the first three minutes at a moderate pace and then speed up for the last three minutes.)

2. Lock your legs in Lotus Pose. Rest your elbows against your rib cage with the forearms pointing upward and the palms facing forward at shoulder level. Rock backward and forward in this position. 2 Minutes.

3. Stand up with your legs spread wide apart. The arms are straight up over head with the palms together. Keeping the palms together and the elbows straight, bend to the left and touch the left toes. Rise up. Bend to the right and touch the right toes. Rise up and continue. 5 1/2 Minutes. This exercise frees up your solar plexus.

4

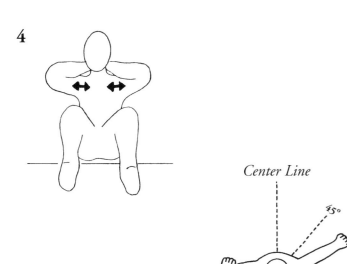

Center Line

45°

Top view of arm motion in #5

5

4. Come into Crow Pose. Lock your hands behind your head with your elbows extended out to the sides. Move your elbows in so that they point straight forward. Then move them back out to the sides. Continue. Move powerfully but keep your balance. 1 Minute.

5. Remain in Crow Pose with your elbows at your rib cage, forearms pointing upward, and the palms facing forward. Extend your right arm up to sixty degrees and out to the side at a sixty degree angle. When the arm is extended fully, close your hand as if you are grabbing something. Pull the right arm back as you extend the left arm up at 60 degrees. When the arm is extended fully, close your hand as if you are grabbing something. Continue this movement for 1 Minute.

Remain in Crow Pose and gather together the tips of the fingers of each hand. Place these fingertips on the top of each shoulder. Raise your elbows up parallel to the floor and begin twisting left and right. 30 Seconds.

6. Sit in Easy Pose. Inhale and chant "Hari Har, Hari Har, Hari Har, Haree" in a monotone. One repetition of the mantra takes two seconds. 30 Seconds.

To finish: Inhale, hold the breath 20-30 seconds and exhale. Repeat this breath two more times and then relax.

"The flexible spine holds your entire nervous system"
YB

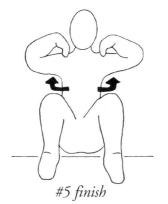

#5 finish

"The spine needs flexibility and balance. This precise series of exercises coordinates the movement and flexibility of the sacrum and lower spine with the upper spine and the occiput (the back of the skull). The result is strength, balance, and endurance." GCSK

8

Balancing the Three Psyches

5-24-84

Projectivity in Kundalini Yoga balances the intelligence. Sometimes the psyche of intelligence is not balanced with the psyche around you. There are three psyches: your individual inner psyche, the psyche which is in your immediate environment, and the psyche of the landscape which is bigger, higher, and wider. If these three psyches are not in balance, you are not in harmony.

The problem with you is that you think money can make you harmonious, you think relationships can make you harmonious, you think power can make you harmonious, but if your own psyche is not in harmony, nothing can make you harmonious.

Kundalini Yoga works on eight centers, the seven chakras and the one engulfing aura. Lots of Kundalini Yoga masters have been taught about the chakras. They have not been taught about the arc line and the aura. Therefore the science is not complete with them. That is why for centuries it has been told that Kundalini yoga should not be taught because it is dangerous. It is only dangerous if you open up the chakras without the controlling connection of the aura and the arc line. There are ten bodies and they all have to be in balance.

"Between human and God there is an opening door and the key to that door is called Kundalini."

YB

1

1. Come onto your hands and knees in Cow Pose. Extend your left leg behind you and raise it to sixty degrees. Point and flex the left foot in rhythm with a powerful Breath of Fire. The breath and the foot move at the same speed. 3 Minutes. Change legs and continue the exercise.
1 1/2 Minutes. As you do this exercise you will find a surprising energy moving through you.

2

2. Come onto your hands and knees in Cat Pose. Make a fist of your left hand in front of your heart center and begin punching your fist forward in rhythm with Breath of Fire. The hand and arm are as tough as steel, the punch is strong, and the breath is rhythmic and powerful. The shoulder blade must move.
2 Minutes. Change arms and continue the exercise.
1 1/2 Minutes.

3

3. Sit on your heels. Bow and touch your forehead to the floor at the same time that you powerfully clap your hands behind your back. Sit up once again in the starting position and continue the movement. 3 1/2 Minutes.

hand position

4

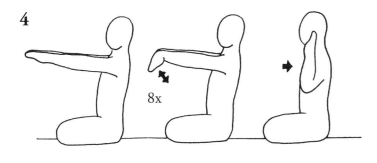

8x

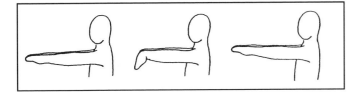

8x wrist movement

4. Sit in Easy Pose with your arms out straight in front parallel to the floor with your palms facing down. Your thumbs are touching the mounds at the base of the Mercury fingers (little fingers). The hands move rapidly up and down at the wrist eight times. (These eight movements should take about 2 seconds). As soon as the eight count is finished, bend your elbows, and rapidly pull your arms back so that the elbows rest on the rib cage, the forearms point upward, and the palms face forward. Then extend your arms and repeat the eight count hand movement. Continue 1 1/2 Minutes.

5. Lie down on your back and relax.

Eliminate Gastric Troubles

February 29, 1984

1

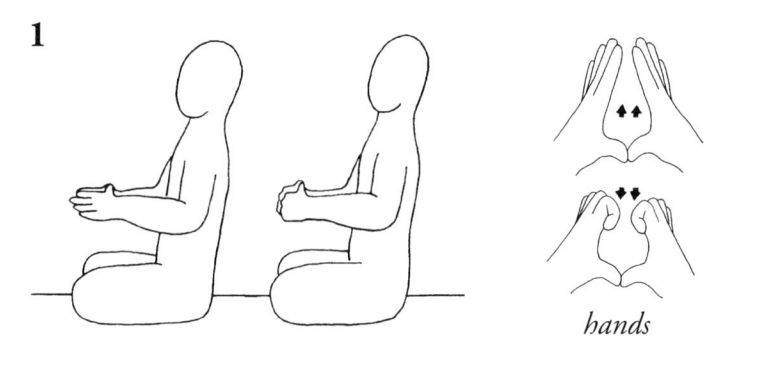

hands

1. Sit in Easy Pose with your upper arms resting against your rib cage and your elbows bent. Your forearms are parallel to the floor and the palms of the hands are facing each other. Your thumbs are touching. Open and close the fingers of both hands at the same time. "Put your mind into it. You are dealing with mental energy as well as physical energy. Combine it." Concentrate deeply and move only your fingers. 4 1/2 Minutes.

If it starts hurting in the middle, that is not a good thing. If it starts hurting at the beginning it is all right, but if it hurts at the end, go see your doctor.

2

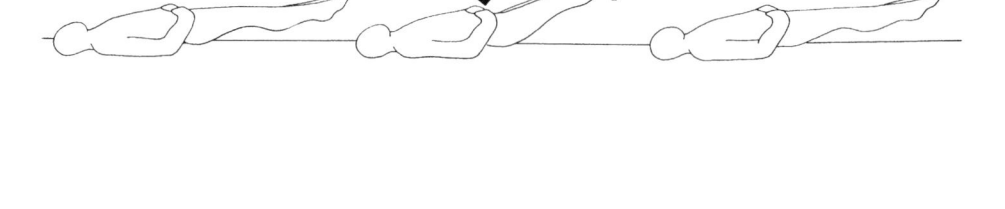

2. Lie down on your back. Keep your head on the floor and raise your heels up six inches. Put your fingers on your navel point. Press hard on your navel with both hands as you raise your heels up to eighteen inches. Relax the pressure and lower your heels back to six inches. It is a foot and a half game. Continue for 3 1/2 Minutes.

3

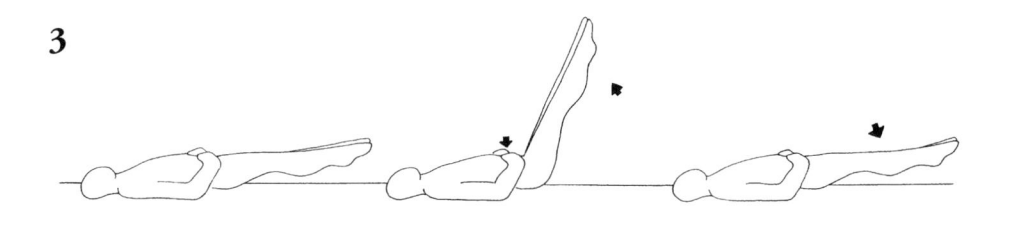

3. Stay in the same position as exercise #2, with your fingers on your navel and your heels at six inches. With a heavy pressure on your navel, raise your heels up to eighty degrees (almost straight up, but not quite). Relax the pressure and lower your heels to six inches. Continue for 2 Minutes. (Starting and ending the movement with the heels at six inches off the floor is to benefit the sciatica.)

4

5

6

finish

7

4. Lie down on your back and put your hands under your buttocks, cupping them. Raise your legs up to ninety degrees, spread your legs apart, bring your legs back together, and then lower them to the floor. Continue this movement keeping your knees straight. 3 Minutes.

5. Still on your back, put your hands under your neck directly against the skin. Make sure your hands are under your neck and not under your head. Begin alternately lifting each leg up to ninety degrees and lowering it to the floor. 1 1/2 Minutes.

6. Still on your back, raise both legs up to ninety degrees, keeping your knees straight, and your heels together. Grasp your toes with both hands. Stay in the position and chant: "Aap Sahaaee Hoaa, Sachay Daa, Sachaa Dhoaa, Har, Har, Har."
7 Minutes.

Inhale, hold your breath 15 seconds, and stretch your legs over your head into Plow Pose. Exhale and relax down.

7. Sit up and spread your legs as far apart as you can. Grab your toes. Stretch your torso forward and down toward the floor. In this position gently and gradually stretch down farther for eight counts (about 3 seconds). Then bring your torso up straight for one count. Bend forward again and continue. Move your lower back to open it up and get rid of pain. 1 Minute.

"Problem is not me. Problem is my stress which I cause to me."

YB

12

Exercising the Central Vagus Nerve

June 20, 1984

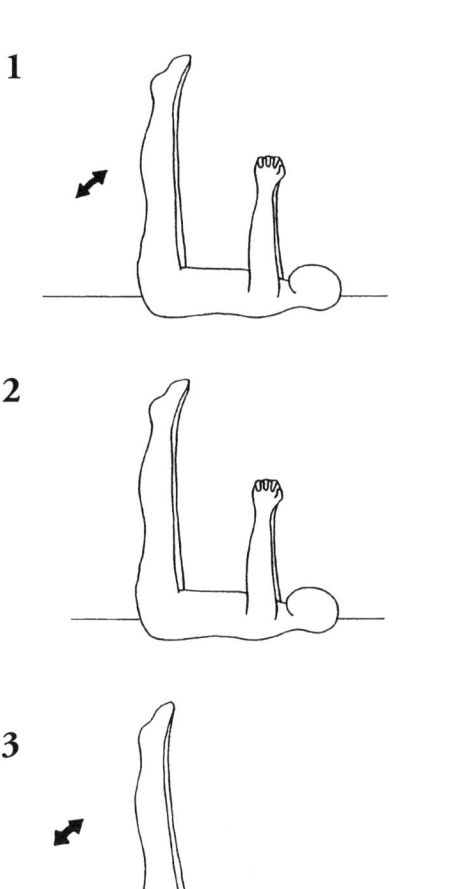

All movements are to be done vigorously. One complete up and down movement of the legs in exercises 1-5 should take only about 4 seconds.

1. Lie down on your back, raise both arms up to 90 degrees, and interlock your fingers. Begin leg lifts, raising both legs up to 90 degrees, and lowering them. The arms do not move. They remain up with no bend in the elbows. Move with power. 9 1/2 Minutes.

2. Stop the movement with the legs up at 90 degrees and hold the position. 1 1/2 Minutes.

3. Still lying on your back, stretch your arms out on the ground above your head. Resume leg lifts, raising both legs up to 90 degrees, and lowering them. 1 1/2 Minutes.

4. Remain lying on your back with your arms stretched on the ground above your head. Raise your legs up to 90 degrees. Spread your legs one foot apart and keep them spread as you lower them to the ground. When they touch the ground, bring them together and raise them back up to 90 degrees. Continue this movement: legs together when they go up, legs spread apart one foot when they go down. 30 Seconds.

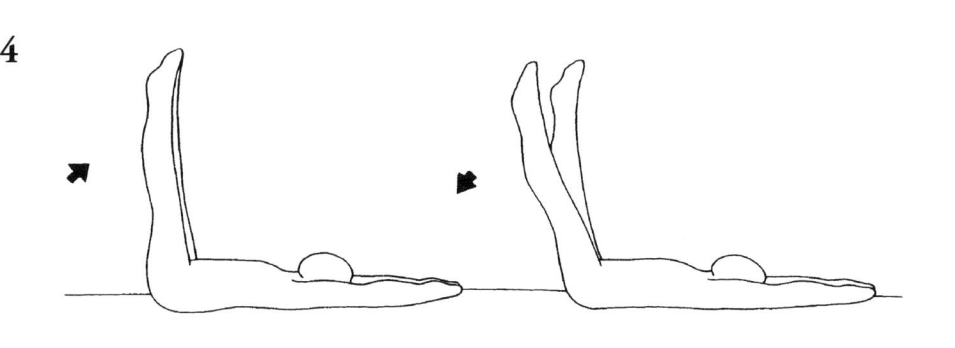

5

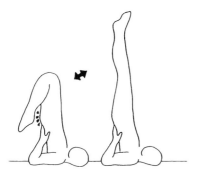

6

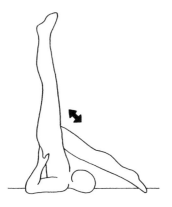

7

5. Come into Shoulder Stand. Bend your knees and bring your heels to your buttocks. Then immediately raise your legs back up into Shoulder Stand. Keep your legs together as they move up and down. Continue for 2 Minutes.

6. From Shoulder Stand, bring your legs alternately down to touch the floor behind your head. As one leg goes down, the other leg goes back up. 1 Minute. Begin chanting "Sa-Ta-Na-Ma" with the movement. "Sa" and touch one foot to the ground. "Ta" and touch the other foot to the ground. "Na" and touch the first foot to the ground. "Ma" and touch the other foot to the ground.
2 1/2 Minutes.

7. Come into Plow Pose, holding onto your feet with your hands.
30 Seconds.
Chant "God and Me, Me and God Are One" in this position 1 Minute. (This is the best posture for chanting this mantra.)

8. Lie down on your back and relax, consciously going through all the parts of your body and turning off excess tension. 15 Minutes.

"In Kundalini Yoga, you reach to a source of energy within yourself that you can organically use."

YB

14

Exercises to Create a Disease-Free Body

June 18, 1984

1

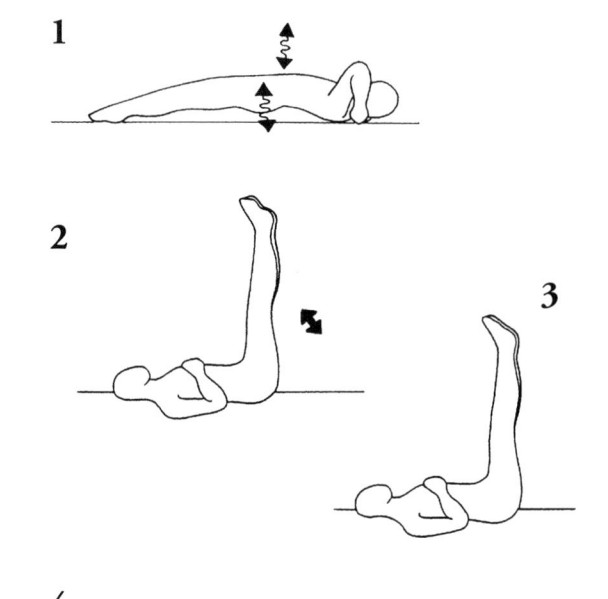

2

3

4

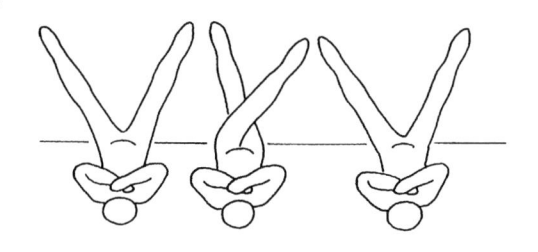

5

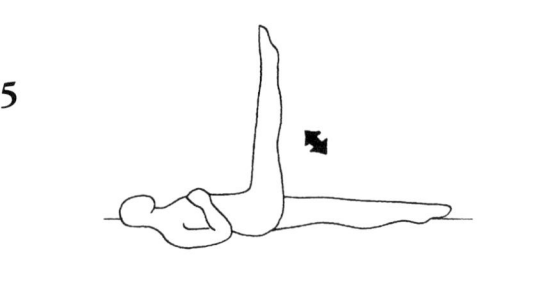

6

1. Lie down flat on your back with your legs straight and your heels touching. Your hands are under your neck, touching the skin. Move your hips left and right and up and down like a jumping bean. Move vigorously. After 2 1/2 Minutes begin Breath of Fire and continue the movement for an additional 1 Minute.
This movement stimulates the nervous system which ultimately is the base power. If the base power is well stimulated, human effectiveness is greater that otherwise.

2. Remain on your back with your legs straight and your heels touching. Cross your hands over your heart center. Inhale through your nose and raise your legs up to 90 degrees. Exhale through your mouth as you lower your legs. Continue these leg lifts for 5 Minutes. Hand over hand at the heart center is the most neutral energy posture possible.

3. Keep your hands in the same position and lift your legs up to 90 degrees. Hold this position. Listen to Kulwant Singh's *Jaap Sahib: Last Four Lines* as you inhale through the nose and exhale through the mouth for 2 Minutes. Hold the position and begin to sing along with the tape for an additional 3 Minutes. Sing from the rib cage. Sing from the heart.

4. Keeping your legs up at 90 degrees and your hands crossed over your heart, criss-cross your legs. Continue singing. 7 Minutes.

5. Keep your hands in the same position and raise each leg alternately to 90 degrees. As one leg goes up, the other leg goes down. Bring the legs all the way to the ground. Keep the knees straight. Continue singing. 4 Minutes.

6. Sit in easy pose with your arms up in the air with your palms facing forward. Begin opening and closing your arms, criss-crossing them over your head. Keep the elbows straight. Continue singing with the tape. 7 minutes.
Continue the movement but, instead of singing, inhale through the nose and exhale through the mouth. 2 Minutes.
"Stimulate the lymph glands to get the poison out. It is a prayer. Move your hands to create a vacuum pressure to move the Kundalini Shakti up. Do it with sacredness."

7

8

10

11

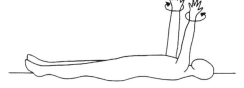

7. Sit in easy pose with your hands on your shoulders. Twist left and right, moving from the hips. Vigorously move the rib cage. Inhale through the nose, exhale through the mouth for 2 1/2 Minutes. Then begin singing for the last 1 1/2 Minutes.

8. Lie on your back, bend your legs, bring your knees to your chest. Extend the legs straight out allowing the heels to touch the ground. When the feet touch the ground, bring the knees back to the chest. Continue the movement for 3 Minutes. This exercise can help to relieve gas.
If your knees don't obey you, you can use your hands to press your knees to your chest.

9. Relax every part of your body. Meditatively move through your body, relaxing each part. Remain relaxed and motionless, allowing your body to recuperate. Fly away from your body. Meditate on the heavens, beauty, and excellence. Don't move for any reason. 8 1/2 Minutes.
During this layout Yogi Bhajan played Kulwant Singh's *Jaap Sahib: Last Four Lines* for 5 Minutes and then 3 1/2 Minutes of Singh Kaur's "Beloved God" from the *Peace Lagoon* tape.

10. Remain on your back and rotate your wrists and your ankles. 2 Minutes.

11. Remain on your back and raise your arms straight up to 90 degrees with the fingers wide open. Your feet are relaxed, resting on the floor. 30 Seconds. Move your arms in circles with no bend in the elbows. 1 Minute.

12. Relax.

"When your circulation is strong, disease doesn't like to visit you. This set moves your blood, lymph, and prana. It activates the nervous system from the navel center, distributing energy so you can relax and live fear-free and full of health." GCSK

"Spirit is stronger than the physical body."
YB

16

Exercises for the Heart Center

April 11, 1984

1

1. Come into Cobra Pose and hold the position for 30 Seconds. Then raise and lower your chin Sixteen Times. This is to test your ability to withstand stress.

2

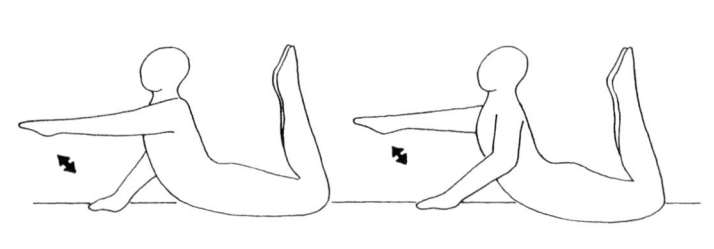

2. Still in Cobra Pose, bend your knees so that your feet are up by your head. Lift your hands alternately up to your shoulders. You should feel the stretch under your rib cage. 2 Minutes.

3. Repeat Exercise #2, but this time alternately raise and lower your entire arm. Raise one arm straight up, lower it, and raise the other arm straight up and continue for 1 1/2 Minutes.

3

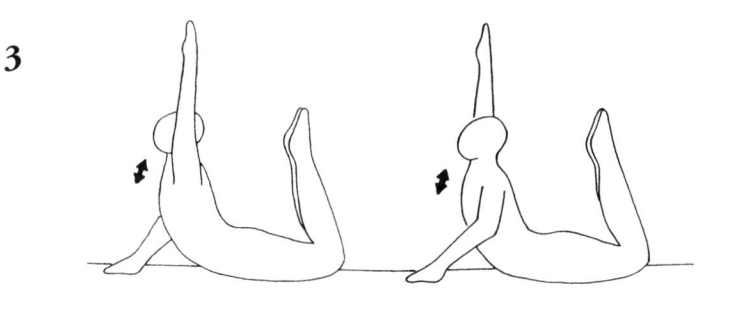

4. Lying on your stomach, interlace your fingers behind your back, arch the upper body, and lift the hands as high as possible. Inhale through your nose and exhale through your mouth as forcefully as you can. 2 Minutes. This powerful breath combined with the posture and movement can strengthen your spine and nervous system.

5. Come into Bow Pose and rock back and forth on your stomach. 2 Minutes. This exercise can renew every tissue of the body when done correctly.

6. Lie flat on your back, use your arms to hug your knees to your chest, and roll on your spine. 1 Minute.

4

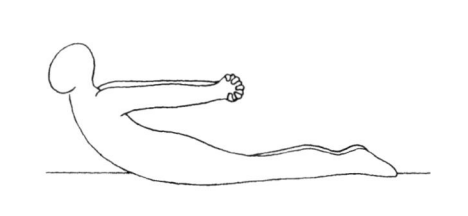

5

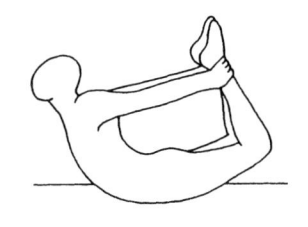

6

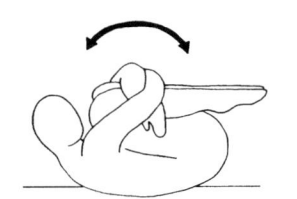

7

8

9

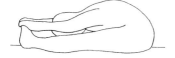

10

7. Lie flat on your back and bring both legs up to ninety degrees. Keep your knees straight, toes pointed upward, and the posture steady. Relax the rest of your body. 2 Minutes.

8. Still lying on your back, place your hands on the floor under your shoulders and arch your torso up, keeping your hips and legs on the floor. Stretch your toes forward. 2 1/2 Minutes. This exercise is designed to give power to the heart muscle.

9. Sit up with your legs stretched forward and catch hold of your toes. Stretch your torso forward and hold the position. 1 Minute.

10. Sit in Crow Pose with your arms out straight in front. Raise your arms alternately up to ninety degrees. 2 Minutes. This exercise can save you from intestinal bloating in old age.

11. Sit peacefully in Easy Pose like a yogi. Keep your eyes open, inhaling and exhaling deeply. After 1 Minute close your eyes and continue the breath. After 1 more minute, bring your mind to thoughtlessness. Continue in the thoughtless meditation for 3 1/2 more minutes.
Then begin to chant Chattr Chakkr Vartee along with the tape *Jaap Sahib:Last Four Lines* by Kulwant Singh .
6 Minutes.

Chattr Chakkr vartee, chattr chakkr bhugatay
Suyumbhav subhang, sarab daa sarab jugatay
Dukaalang pranaasee, dayaalang saroopay
Sadaa ang sangay, abhangang bibhootay.

"All the exercises in this set work on the heart muscle and the heart center. They concentrate on one power of energy like a storehouse." Yogi Bhajan said that you may extend the time for each of these exercises to 7 Minutes, to make the set complete. This length of practice will put you into a restful state of mind. You will want to sleep, so allow for this extra rest time when doing the extended version of this set.

"Chattr Chakkr Vartee" is the mantra for the heart center, it gives direct energy to it. When you are sinking, if you know this mantra and can sing it, you can totally recuperate yourself."
YB

18

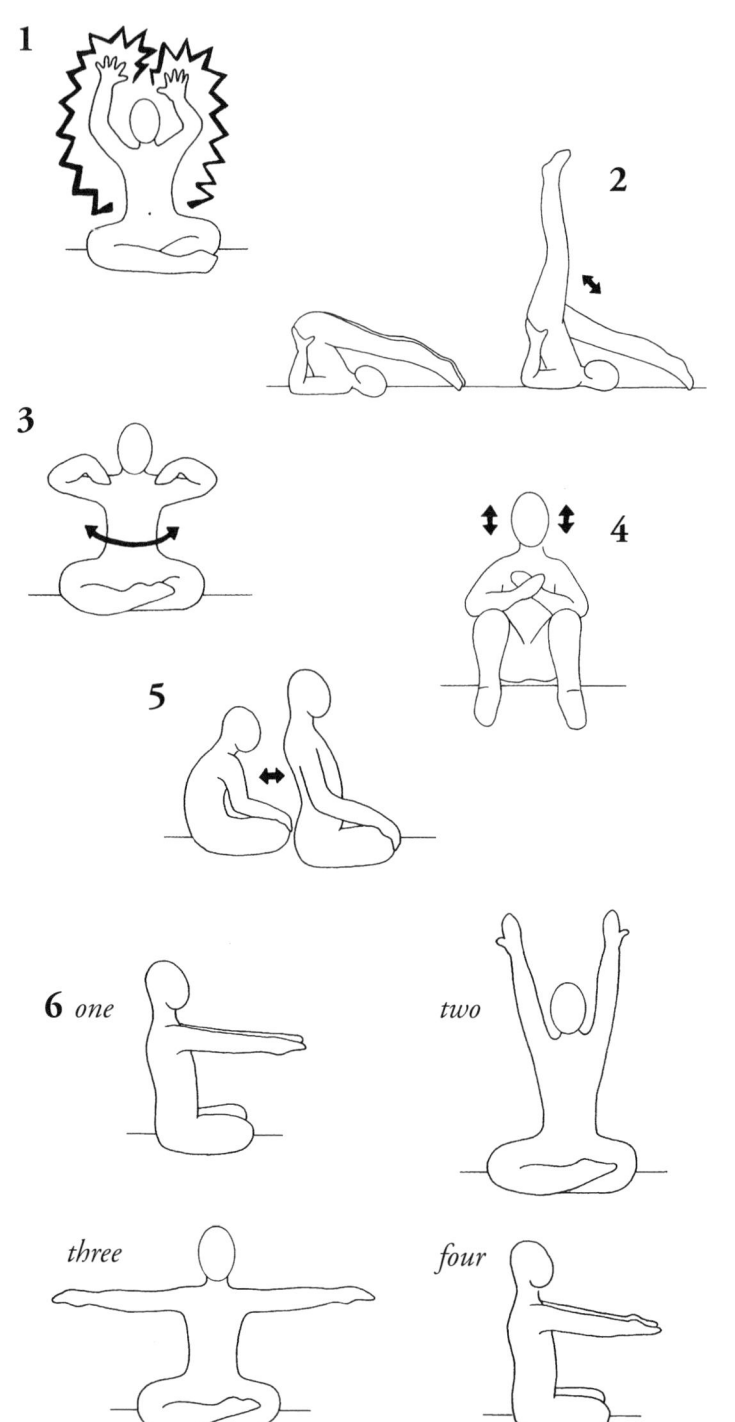

For the Third Chakra and Glandular System

5-23-84

1. Sit in Easy Pose and raise your arms up into the air. Dance your body from the navel point to the tips of the fingers. Pump your navel rhythmically in coordination with your movement. Move your arms, shoulders, and rib cage. Move with great energy and invigorate all of your ten trillion cells. 8 Minutes.

2. Come into Plow Pose, supporting your hips with your hands. Raise your left leg up to ninety degrees and lower it as you raise your right leg up to ninety degrees. Continue alternate leg lifts. 2 Minutes.

3. Sit in Easy Pose. Grasp the shoulders with the fingers in front and the thumbs behind. Inhale and twist to the left. Exhale and twist to the right. Keep the upper arms parallel to the floor. Move vigorously for 2 Minutes.

4. Squat down in Crow Pose and place both hands at the center of your chest. Stand up and squat down. Continue for 2 Minutes.

5. Sit in Easy Pose with your hands on your knees. Flex your spine forward as you inhale and flex your spine backward as you exhale. Move vigorously. 1 Minute.

6. Sit in Easy Pose and move into each position at the count:
  One: Bring your arms straight out in front of you with your palms down.
  Two: Bring your arms straight up with your palms turned backwards.
  Three: Bring your arms straight out to the sides with your palms down.
  Four: Bring your arms straight out in front with your palms up.
  Continue this sequence of movements for 4 Minutes.

This exercise is to balance the brain using the hands. It brings a coordination between relaxing and working. (When this exercise is done in a class, the challenge is to only move after hearing the count. This connects the message system of the brain with the motor system of the brain.)

7 *one*　　　　　　　　　　*two*

three　　　　　　　　　　*four*

9 *one*　　　　　　　　　　*two*

three　　　　　　　　　　*four*

7. Sit in Easy Pose and move into each position at the count:
  One: Bring your arms straight out in front of you with your palms down.
  Two: Lift your left arm up to ninety degrees, keeping the right arm straight. Begin moving the right arm up and down 18", without bending the elbow.
  Three: Keep the right arm moving as you bring the left arm straight out to the side with the palm down.
  Four: Bring your arms straight out in front with your palms down.
  Continue this sequence of movements for 2 Minutes.

8. Change arms and repeat Exercise #7 for 30 seconds.

9. Still sitting in Easy Pose, interlace the fingers and rest them on the top of your head.
  One: Circle your body to the right bringing your forehead to the floor.
  Two: In this position, raise your forehead only.
  Three: Circle your body to the left, coming back into a sitting position.
  Four: Bring your chin to your chest.
Continue this sequence of movements, circling to the right, for 1 Minute. Then reverse directions, repeating the sequence of movements, but circling to the left for 1 Minute.

10. Lie down on your back with your legs straight and your toes pointing upward. Lift your legs up twelve inches from the floor. Move into each position at the count, keeping your feet twelve inches from the floor throughout:
  One: point your right foot forward.
  Two: point your left foot forward.
  Three: Point your right foot straight up
  Four: Point your left foot straight up.
Continue this sequence of movements for 2 1/2 Minutes.

10 *one*　　　　　　　　*two*　　　*three*　　　*four*

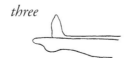

20

11

12

13 *one*   *two*

three   *four*

14

21

11. Remain on your back and raise your arms up to ninety degrees. Move your arms in a scissor motion in line with your body. As your right arm moves up toward your head, your left arm moves down toward your feet. Then your left arm moves up toward your head as your right arm moves down toward your feet. 1 Minute.

12. Lying on your back, bend your knees and put your feet flat on the floor. Reach down and grab your heels. Begin raising and lowering your buttocks. 2 1/2 Minutes.

13. Lie down on your back with your hands under your buttocks and your legs stretched out straight. Move into each position at the count:
    One : Lift your torso up sixty degrees from the floor.
    Two: Bring your torso straight up to ninety degrees.
    Three: Bend forward to sixty degrees from the floor.
    Four: Bend forward touching your forehead to your knees.
    Zero: Return to the starting position, lying on your back.
Continue this sequence of movements for 2 1/2 Minutes.

14. Lie down in Baby Pose with your head turned to the left. Chant the Adi Shakti mantra "Ek Ong Kaar-a, Sa Ta Naa-ma, Siree Waa-ha, Hay Guroo" in the three and a half cycle Laya Yoga manner. On "Ek" pull the navel point. The last syllable of "Kaar-a", "Naa-ma", and "Waa-ha", is created by sharply pulling in and up on the diaphragm. On "Hay Guroo", relax the lock. Visualize the sound spinning around the spine from its base to the top of the head.
2 1/2 Minutes.

15. Lie on your back and relax, concentrating at your brow point.
7 Minutes.

16. While still on your back, swing your body from side to side moving like a crocodile. 30 Seconds.
Slowly rise up into a sitting position without using your hands. Relax.

"Price of nobility is discipline. Price of ecstacy is sadhana. Price of God is living without doubt."
YB

11-14-84

1

"We don't need Free Will. We need the free flow of energy so we can handle our life when it is challenged."

YB

2

3

1. Come onto your hands and knees in Cow Pose. Remain balanced in Cow Pose, as you rapidly bring both hands back to touch your buttocks, and then return your hands to the floor. Continue. Maintain a fast pace which will create its own special breath rhythm. 3 1/2 Minutes. At this point continue the movement while adding a "long" Breath of Fire, that is, your Breath of Fire is coordinated with the movement so that the movement is at the speed of your rapid, heavy breath. 2 1/2 Minutes.
If the most impotent, depressed person can keep his balance in cow pose and touch the back of the buttocks to give stimulus to the sciatica "pinch point", and then return to cow pose, he can totally re-invigorate himself.

2. Lie down on your back. Meditate on the celestial echo sound of the gong as played by Yogi Bhajan, using the tape of this class. Contract the navel with each hit of the gong, hold it until the next hit of the gong, then release it and rapidly contract it again. 4 Minutes.
In order to receive the benefits of this kriya, it is required that this exercise be done to the exact gong meditation that Yogi Bhajan played in class. (See the Introduction for where to purchase this tape.)

3. Rise up, stretch your arms up and vigorously shake your hands. 15 Seconds.

22

May 31, 1984

1

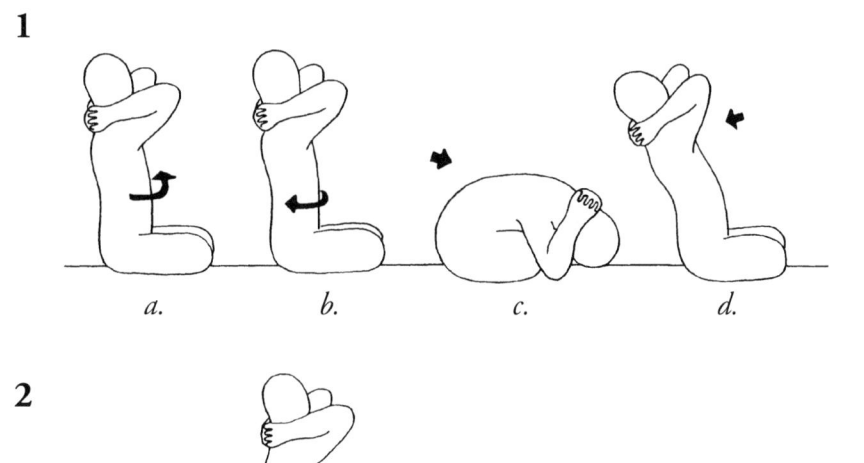

a.   b.   c.   d.

2

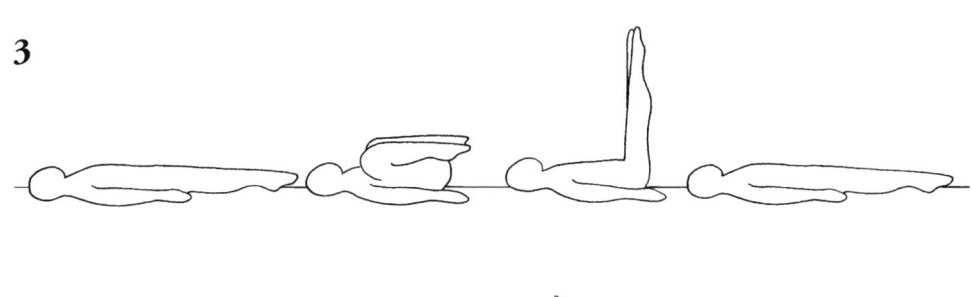

3

4

1. Sitting in Easy Pose, lock your hands behind your neck with the elbows out to the sides. Keep the neck straight, don't allow your hands to push it forward.
a. Twist your torso to the left.
b. Twist your torso to the right.
c. Bend your torso straight forward (bringing your forehead to the floor).
d. Bend your torso backward as far as you possibly can, without allowing your legs to lift up.
Continue this sequence of movements. Move vigorously.
6 Minutes

2. Still in the same posture, bend your torso forward, bringing your forehead to the floor, and come back up. Move as rapidly as you can. 2 Minutes. This exercise helps the brain to replenish its own blood supply. The muscles responsible for doing this can only be activated if the movement is done vigorously.

3. Lie down flat on your back with your hands on the floor at your sides. Bring both knees to the chest, then extend both legs straight up to ninety degrees, and then lower them back to the floor. Continue. The complete cycle of movement should take two seconds. Breathe in and out heavily in time with the movement so your breath becomes like Breath of Fire. 1 1/2 Minutes.

4. Still lying on your back, interlock your hands behind your head with the elbows out to the sides. Bring your elbows and legs up to ninety degrees at the same time. Continue raising and lowering the elbows and legs with Breath of Fire. 1 1/2 Minutes.

5

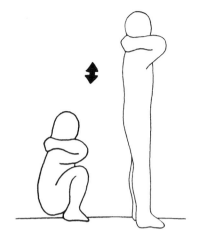

6

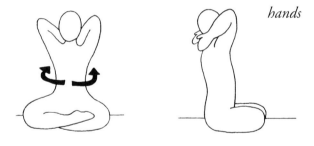

hands

7

5. Squat down with your heels on the ground. Lock your hands behind your neck. Stand up and return to the squatting position, moving at a rate of one movement per second. This is for detoxification. 2 Minutes.

6. In Easy Pose, put the backs of the hands on your neck at a point between the sides and the back of the neck. (If your neck were square, your hands would be on the back corners.) Your elbows are up and point forward. In this position, twist the torso left and right. 2 Minutes.
This exercise is called the "C-spring", because, if done correctly, it can adjust vertebrae C-1 to C-7.

7. Still in Easy Pose, extend your arms straight out in front, parallel to the floor with your palms facing down. Make your hands into fists. Extend your body forward, keeping the arms parallel to the floor. Pull your fists back to your chest with heavy tension as your torso leans backward. The movement is like rowing a boat. It is called "parallel stretch move".
2 Minutes.

8. Relax and sit like a Yogi. 30 Seconds.
Begin to chant rapidly in a monotone: Har, Har, Wahe Guru. 1 repetition of the mantra takes 2 seconds. Continue for 2 1/2 Minutes.

To finish: Inhale, hold the breath 18 seconds. Exhale. Repeat this sequence two more times.

"This body, mind, and spirit is yours. Enjoy it or waste it. It is your choice."

YB

Glandular System

June 12, 1984

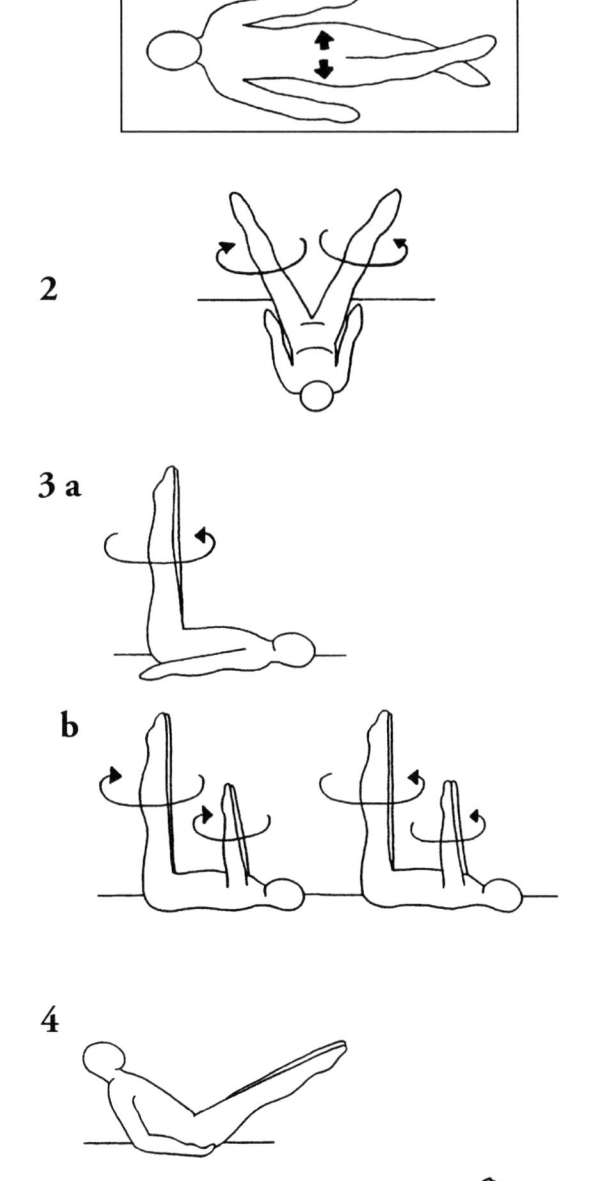

1

2

3 a

b

4

1. Lie down on your back and cross your legs at the ankles. Move your hips from side to side, isolating the movement so that only your hips move. Don't twist your hips, move them from side to side. You must move powerfully. This is no small exercise; it is helpful to the kidneys, adjusts the glandular system, and can help you to recover from glandular depletion. 2 1/2 Minutes.

2. Remain on your back and bring your legs up to ninety degrees, keeping your knees straight. Move each leg in individual circles. Both legs move at the same time but they make separate circles. This adjusts the basic pelvic rotation which normally gets out, making you old and causing shortness of breath. This is a good exercise to do every day. 2 1/2 Minutes.

3. In the same position:
a. Bring your legs together and move them in a circle together for 3 Minutes.
b. Continue the leg movement, bring your arms up to ninety degrees, and move them in a circle at the same time. First rotate your arms and legs in a clockwise direction 21 times and then rotate them 21 times in a counter-clockwise direction. Coordinate the movement of the arms and legs. Then relax down and stretch your legs.
This exercise keeps you going, flowing, and young. It should make your cheeks red.

4. Still lying on your back, put your heels together, and place your hands under your buttocks. Raise your upper body and your legs up until your nose and toes are directly across from each other. Hold this position for 30 Seconds. Then bring your nose to your knees and return to the "nose and toes directly across from each other" position. Continue moving up and down. 2 1/2 Minutes.

If you do this exercise correctly and practice regularly, you can never have a headache, no matter what. It brings balance to the function of the brain and all the tissues.
(Those who wish to do the advanced version of this exercise may lie down flat on their backs after touching their nose to knees and continue going up and down that way.)

5

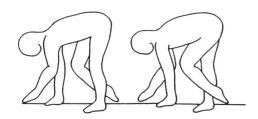

5. Balance yourself in the all-fours position on your hands and feet. Lift your left hand and your right foot at the same time. Then lower them and lift your right hand and left foot at the same time. Continue lifting alternate hands and feet for 3 Minutes. Continue the same movement but move like you are dancing for 30 Seconds. This exercise is very good for circulation and wonderful for the nerves.

6

6. Sit in Easy Pose, with one hand over the other at the heart center. Revolve the torso on the hips in a grinding motion. Make a heavy complete revolution of your spine. Give yourself a chance to unclog your liver. 4 1/2 Minutes.

7. Stand up, close your eyes, and dance. Dance any way you feel like, use any rhythm, but keep your balance. Keep your eyes closed throughout the dance. Meditate on the fact that the whole world is dancing with you. Dance so that you feel hot breath in your nostrils. The breath should become fiery from the energy that you put into this dance. 9 1/2 Minutes

8. Sit down in Easy Pose and raise your arms up over your head with the fingers interlaced and the elbows straight. Move your arms in a wild and powerful circle over your head. 1 Minute.

7

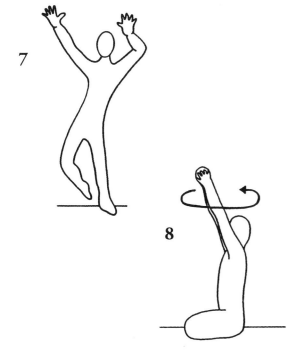

8

9. Relax your arms down and sit like a yogi. Chant long "Sat Nam's." Inhale, chant "Sat" extending the sound, then chant "Nam" in a short syllable. (If the "Sat" is chanted for 35 beats, then the "Nam" is chanted for 1 beat, that is the proportion.) 2 Minutes. Chant "Wah-hay Guroo, Wah-hay Guroo, Wah-hay Guroo" continuously in a monotone for 2 Minutes. Chant at a moderate pace and be sure to chant in three parts "Wah," "Hay," "Guroo." Chant "Har Har Haree, Har Har Haree" for 30 Seconds.

To finish: Inhale deeply, bring your hands into Prayer Mudra at the heart center, hold your breath 30 seconds, while you meditate on the energy of the heart and hands together. Exhale. Inhale, hold your breath 30 seconds, and continue to meditate on the energy of the heart and hands. Exhale. Inhale, hold your breath 30 seconds, and concentrate on your third eye point. Exhale and relax.

"Where the Kundalini is, the entire wealth of the universe and the heavens is. Where the Kundalini is awakened, all corners bring gifts and salutations. It is the most divine power of God himself. It is God's thunderbolt."

YB

1

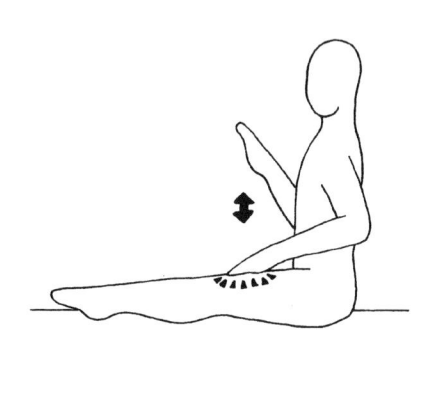

2 & 4

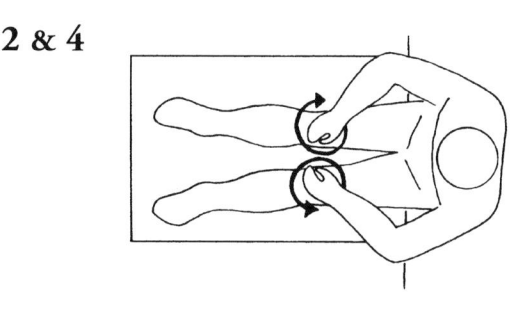

3

5

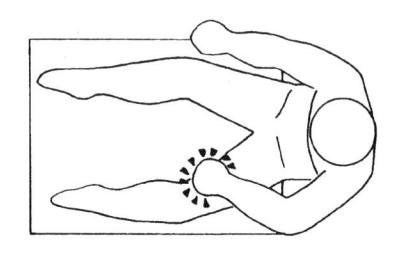

August 22, 1986

This is a good set of exercises to do every day, because if the body's energy is not released, circulated, and distributed, then it will start malfunctioning.

1. Sit with your legs straight out in front of you. Using both hands alternately, begin hitting the tops of your thighs. 30 Seconds. The point you are stimulating is where the 3rd Meridian, liver, and kidney meet.

2. Keeping the legs stretched out straight, cup your kneecaps with each hand. Massage each kneecap with a circular motion. Massage with force and motion. 2 Minutes. Just doing this simple movement, see how much energy you can release, control, and feel good about.

    Underneath the kneecap regulates and sustains your body's water. Too much water in your system can create headaches; too little water can create bitchiness and itchiness without reason. Your knee has an important effect on your well-being. The majority of us walk incorrectly and the knees take tremendous stress.

3. Find the point one hand width below the knee on the outside of each calf, right below where the fibula bone protrudes. Vigorously pound the muscle at that point on each side. 2 Minutes.

    This is a general energy point in acupuncture. Stimulating it can totally change your metabolism. After the first minute, pound harder and heavier for the second minute.

4. Repeat Exercise #2 massaging your knees for 10 seconds.

5. Find the point one hand width above the knee on the inside of the thigh. Make fists of your hands and alternately pound the muscle at that point on each side. 1 Minute.

    This is a sex point. It may hurt in some cases. It will let you know that there is something happening in your spine, in your shoulders, and in your head. It has a direct relationship with your pituitary.

6

7

8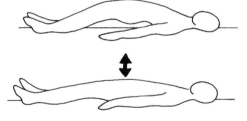

9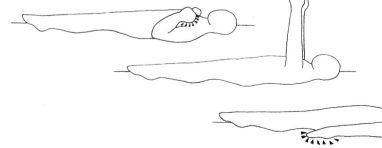

6. Spread the legs wide apart, grab the outside of your ankles with your fingers holding your achilles tendons strongly. Move your torso up and down between your legs, keeping your knees straight. Move fast. 1 1/2 Minutes. (An alternate position for this exercise is sitting in full lotus holding onto your big toes.) Move fast like a propeller that moves so fast that nobody can see the blades. This balances the flow of energy in the spine. Move with a rhythm as fast as you can.

7. Sit in easy pose. Steeple your hands, touching fingertips to fingertips at the heart center. Rotate the joined fingertips together, moving the fingertips in a circular motion while the wrists stay steady. 1 Minute.

   Previous action will have little benefit unless you do this exercise. It sends the energy equally to 72,000 nerve channels, just by doing this. Kundalini energy or the spiral force, the diagonal force, can be moved to every part of the body just by this, providing you have correctly stimulated the energy to begin with.

8. Lie down on your back with your arms on the floor beside your body, palms down. Begin rapidly raising and lowering your hips. This motion will bounce your buttocks against the floor, giving them a vigorous massage. Create a sound like the hoofbeats of galloping horses. 2 Minutes. Move fast, have a beautiful intercourse with God.

9. Still lying on your back, make your hands into fists. Bend your elbows and hit your shoulders with your fists. Then raise your arms straight up to ninety degrees. Keep your arms straight and lower them back down to your sides, hitting the ground hard with your open palms. Make your hands back into fists once again, hit your shoulders, and continue the sequence. 1 Minute.

10. Still on your back alternately hit your chest with your open palms. 1 Minute.

11. Still on your back, alternately tap your forehead with your open palms. 30 Seconds.

28

12

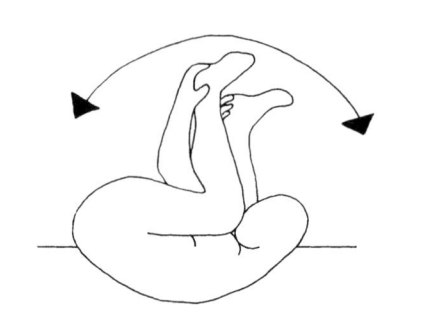

13

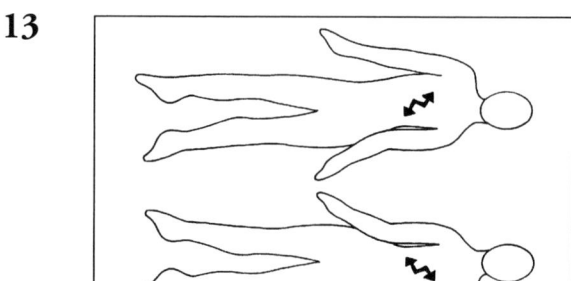

15

16

12. Still on your back, bring your arms and legs into chair pose. Hold your heels and roll back and forth on your spine. 1 Minute. Roll along your whole spine, from your hips to your neck. This will equalize the energy in your spine and will comfort your lower area.

13. Still on your back, move like a snake. Your hips move in one direction while your shoulders and rib cage move in the other direction. Start out just moving one-hundredth millimeter in each direction. This is a very small and precise movement. 2 Minutes. "Move excellently in a curly-whirly way, a small movement with force. Bottom to top. Move heavily back and forth. Give the spinal energy its own chance to move and give the vertebrae an adjustment."

14. Relax, lie down flat, and breathe slowly and deeply at your navel point. 1 1/2 Minutes.

15. Cat stretch slowly left and right. 1 Minute.

16. Lying flat on your back, pull your chin in and raise your head and neck up. Leave your shoulders relaxed on the floor. Your hands are flat on the floor at your sides. Your body is relaxed, but your neck is stretched and tense. 1 Minute.

17. Relax, close your eyes. Then come sitting up in Easy Pose and assess your body energy. 2 Minutes.

To finish do this brief self massage:
1. Using your thumbs, massage under your cheek bones. 15 Seconds.
2. Use the base of your palms to massage your jaw area in a circular motion. 20 Seconds.
3. Use the first three fingers of each hand to massage the sides of the neck. 10 Seconds.
4. Place your palms over your ears and massage your ears in a circular motion. 30 Seconds.

You can take this class and change anybody you want, anytime you want, including yourself...I'm just telling you how to move the energy in every part of the body systematically.

"When the finite gets to you and you show your Infinity, that is Divinity."
YB

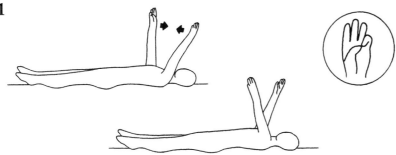

Strengthening the Immune System for Women

10-10-86

1. Lie on your back. Connect the Mercury finger (little finger) and thumb of each hand and criss-cross your arms back and forth over your chest. Your arms open out to the sides, then cross over your chest, and then open out to the sides again. Keep your elbows straight. This movement increase blood circulation in the chest area. 2 Minutes.

2. Keep your arms moving as in #1, pull your knees up, and criss-cross your lower legs from side to side. 2 Minutes.

3. Lie on your back with your arms and legs relaxed. Keep your head on the floor as you turn your head rapidly from side to side. This is the same movement as if you are shaking your head "no." 2 Minutes.

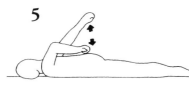

4. Bring your knees to your chest, wrap your arms around them and lift your head up so that your nose is between your knees. Hold the position and do Breath of Fire powerfully. 2 Minutes.

5. Turn over onto your stomach and rapidly hit your buttocks with your fists. This is for youthfulness. 2 Minutes.

6. Come into Bow Pose, balancing on your navel. Hold the position and do Breath of Fire. 2 Minutes. Relax down.

7. Come into Bow Pose again and begin rocking back and forth. 3 Minutes.

8. Relax.

"You are not body. You are not mind. You are not spirit. You are the combining force of these three. You are the commandant in charge of trinity. You are not trinity."

YB

30

The brain has two hemispheres, the left and the right. These two sides must coordinate their activities at the same time to supplement and complement each other. There is another area, called the memory area, that must also coordinate with the two hemispheres of the brain. When this coordination is lacking, the person will be angry, frustrated, and self-destructive.

The things we usually rely on to help us, such as friends, money, youth, and beautiful possessions, are of little importance in life. The important thing is the coordination in action of our brain when we are confronted by the challenge of the times. That is the only friend we need. The rest comes later.

When you encounter a challenging situation and the left initial brain is asked to act, the right brain and the memory should coordinate so that the totality of you will direct the response and the response will be in harmony with who you are.

You may be the most genius person, intelligent, aware, competent, and honest. The whole packet may be perfect. But if the personality through the memory does not reflect the direction in the coordination of the brain hemispheres, you shall not act in full consciousness, in your full self. That is how important this interaction is.

1. Come on to your hands and knees in Cow Pose. Raise your right hand at the same time as you raise your left foot, keeping your left knee on the floor. (The left foot and shin move, but the knee stays on the floor.) Lower your right hand and left foot. Raise your left hand and right foot, keeping your knee on the floor. Continue alternately raising and lowering the opposite hands and feet. 6 Minutes.

Establish a rhythm for this movement and stay with that rhythm as you begin to sing some song you recall from memory. It doesn't matter how fast you go, just keep the rhythm constant. Yogi Bhajan had the class sing the "National Anthem." He suggested using the first pauri of *Jaap Sahib* (Namastang Akaalay) and said that when he learned this exercise, he used the shabd *Dayh Shiva*. Whatever you sing must be recited from memory while maintaining the rhythm of the movement. It is ideal that practice of this exercise is begun at three years of age.

1

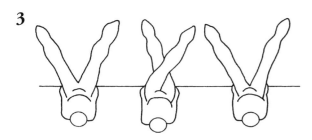

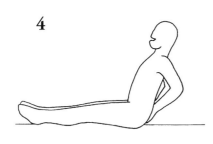

2. Lie on your back. Keep your right leg straight while you bend your left leg, bringing your left knee to your chest. Press your left leg to your chest with your hands for a second. Straighten your left leg and bring your right knee to your chest. By the time your hands press one knee, the other leg should be stretched out. Keep the extended leg out straight a few inches off the floor. Continue alternately pulling each knee to your chest. 4 Minutes.

3. Still lying on your back, bring your legs up to 90 degrees. Open your legs wide and begin criss-crossing them. After 1 Minute, as you continue to open and close your legs, begin a mental speech recounting incidents in your life that made you angry. Recall incidents that have upset you and talk them out mentally. Be sure to keep a steady rhythm in your movement. The exercise dismembers old memories. Continue for another 11-31 Minutes.

4. Remain on your back, place your hands under your lower back and raise your torso up sixty degrees from the floor. Hold the position and smile. Do not rest your weight on your hands or arms. 3 Minutes.

5. Lie down on your back and call someone (anyone) at the top of your lungs. 3 1/2 Minutes.

6. Remain on your back and laugh. 1/2 Minute.

7. Inhale and sit up in Easy Pose. Chant the Adi Shakti mantra "Ek Ong Kaar-a, Sa Ta Naa-ma, Siree Waa-ha, Hay Guroo" in the three and a half cycle Laya Yoga manner.
On "Ek" pull the navel point. The last syllable of "Kaar-a", "Naa-ma", and "Waa-ha", is created by sharply pulling in and up on the diaphragm. On "Hay Guroo", relax the lock. Visualize the sound spinning around the spine from its base to the top of the head. 11-31 Minutes.

To finish: Continue to mentally chant as you inhale 20 seconds, hold your breath for 20 seconds, exhale for 20 seconds. Repeat this breath sequence two more times. Raise your arms into the air and shake them vigorously. Shake the spine and the whole body.

"You have to know your strengths and know your weaknesses. Between your strengths and weaknesses is you."
YB

32

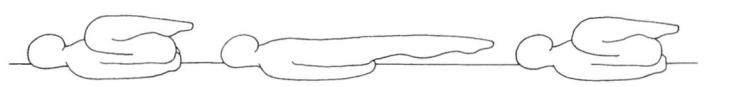

2

3

4 a

b

5

1. Lie on your back. Keep your head on the floor and bring your knees to your chest. Your hands are interlaced around the end of your buttocks. Stretch your legs straight out so that your legs extend parallel to the floor. Bring your knees all the way back to your chest and once again extend your legs. Continue this rhythmic movement for 5 Minutes, then get mad and continue for a further 2 1/2 Minutes. A lot of tension and toxins can be worked out with this exercise, but it may not be comfortable.

2. Sit up in Easy Pose and shake your whole body, moving the arms and rib cage. Don't move artistically, move with force and vigor in all directions. Move the trunk of the body, the shoulders, the whole torso. 4 Minutes.
In these first exercises we are accelerating the energy of the navel point. When the lower part has been straightened out rhythmically, then the upper part should be shaken like an earthquake. Any energy that needs to be adjusted will be adjusted in this looseness. This is called unrhythmic adjustment. It is essential for the rib cage once in a while.

3. Lie down on your left side. Stretch your right leg up and keep it there, while you relax the rest of your body. Pretend you are sleeping, it will give you a natural adjustment. 2 Minutes. Separate yourself, everything is relaxed but the one leg. Change sides. 30 Seconds.

4. Lie down flat on your back.
a. Raise your right arm straight up ninety degrees. Then lower it and raise your left arm up to ninety degrees. Move fast. 2 Minutes. This exercise can put your energy into total balance if you move fast and keep your elbows straight.
b. Raise your right arm and left leg straight up to ninety degrees at the same time. Lower them and raise your left arm and right leg straight up. Continue. 2 Minutes. This exercise is the best thing you can do for your body.

5. Sit in Easy Pose and bring your palms together just above your arcline. (The arcline is an arc of energy over the top of your head reaching from ear tip to ear tip.) Chant long "Akaal." Each Akaal is chanted for approximately 10 seconds. Chant five times.

6. Relax.

"If you can impress the whole world that you can serve them, you will have them in the palm of your hand."

YB

Set to Experience God

November 28, 1984

1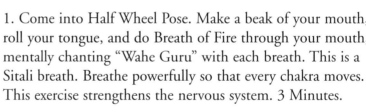

1. Come into Half Wheel Pose. Make a beak of your mouth, roll your tongue, and do Breath of Fire through your mouth, mentally chanting "Wahe Guru" with each breath. This is a Sitali breath. Breathe powerfully so that every chakra moves. This exercise strengthens the nervous system. 3 Minutes.

"Wahe Guru is the mantra of the pituitary gland."
YB

2. Come into a variation of Shoulder Stand. Using your hands to support your lower back firmly, angle your torso up to sixty degrees. Extend your legs up and out so that they are in a straight line with your torso and there is no bend in your back. Keep your knees straight. Your entire weight is on your elbows. Continue the same breath and mantra as in exercise one. This exercise takes care of the entire glandular system. 3 Minutes.

2

3. Come sitting up with your legs spread wide apart and grasp your toes firmly. Continue the same breath and mantra. With each breath, stretch your torso toward the floor and rise back up. Move rapidly. 3 Minutes.

4. Lie down flat on your back. Breathing through your nose, inhale and hold the breath for 20 seconds. Exhale. Repeat this breath nine more times for a total of ten breaths.

5. Move and stretch every part of your body. 45 Seconds.

3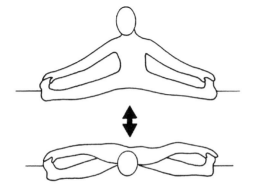

When the first three exercises are done for three minutes each with powerful Breath of Fire through the rolled tongue, they can totally take care of you beyond your belief, expectation, or capacity. Make them a part of your life. Yogi Bhajan said that if you couldn't do Half Wheel Pose in exercise 1, then substitute Bridge Pose.

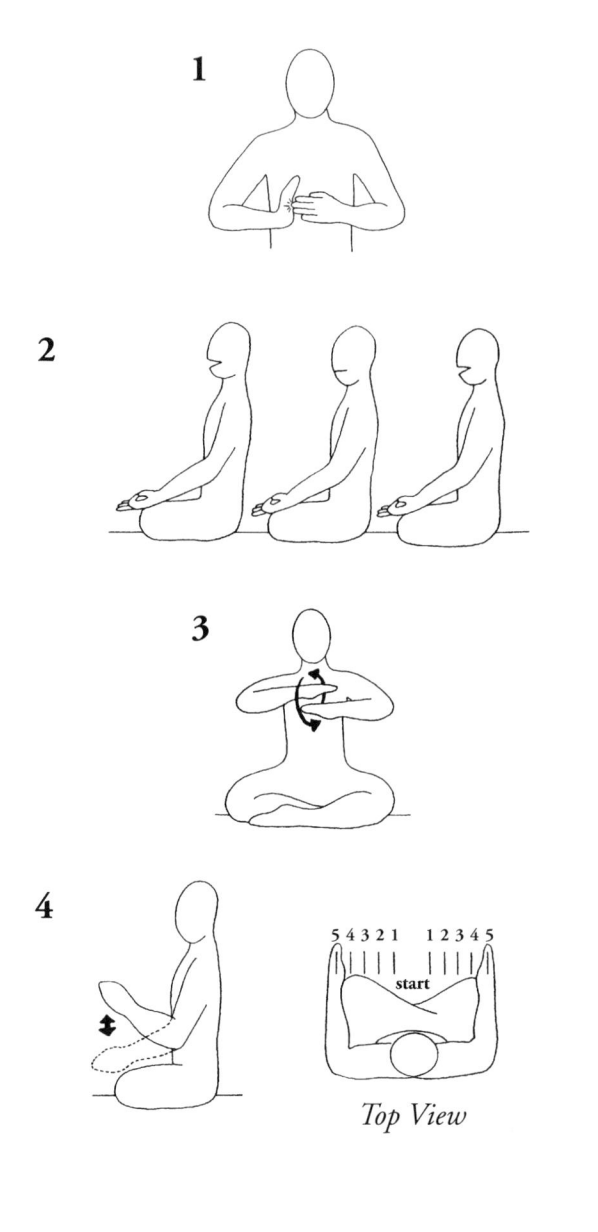

8-23-86

1. Sit in Easy Pose and balance yourself. Bring the fingers of the left hand together and make them stiff. Press the tips of the fingers into the center of the palm of the right hand. Focus the pressure with the Saturn finger and keep adding pressure. With the proper pressure, your palm will become hot. Stretch the spine upward and pump the navel without the breath. (This means to pump the navel either with the breath held in or with the breath held out.) 2 1/2 Minutes.

The energy will start circulating to the areas of weakness and re-balancing them. This is a general tune-up. The easiest and fastest way to recuperate yourself.

2. Sit in Easy Pose with your thumb and Jupiter finger in locked Gian Mudra. It is best if you keep the other fingers straight, but they can be curled. The hands are resting on the knees. Open and close your lips continuously. Don't stop. Don't let the rhythm break. 1 1/2 Minutes. This exercise can help you recover from fatigue.

3. Right hand over left, in front of the heart center, palms facing down. Revolve your hands around each other in a circle, with the palms always facing downward. Do this when you are really worrying and something is really bothering you. 1 1/2 Minutes.

4. Start with your palms facing each other about 4" apart in front of your navel center. Move both hands sharply straight up and down about 8 inches. Spread the hands a little farther apart and again move both hands sharply straight up and down. Spread the hands again and repeat the motion until you have divided your lap into 5 parts, then reverse the direction and continue. 3 Minutes.

It will make you ageless. This exercise is dividing your psyche. Your psyche does not want to be divided, so it will freak out, and try to regroup itself by calling on your reserve energy to balance it out.

Top View

left hand mudra

5. Bring the left hand to the heart center with the palm facing upward, and the Sun (ring) finger touching the thumb. Bring the right arm out to the side and lift it up at a sixty degree angle with the palm up. Turn the palm down and lower the arm. Then turn the palm up and raise the arm back up to sixty degrees. Do this 22 times and then change arms and repeat.

6

6. Steeple your hands, touching the fingertips to fingertips at the heart center. Rotate the joined fingertips together, moving in and out in a circular motion. The wrists stay steady. 11 times.

Take a moment to feel your energy. Our bodies have the power to recuperate themselves. This body is nothing but a bunch of magnetic cells dancing and holding each other.

7

7. Place your hands in front of your heart center. Your hands are in the Open Lotus Mudra with the fingers of the right hand crossing the fingers of the left hand at a 45 degree angle, palms up. Inhale through your nose. Then exhale so powerfully through your nose that you can feel the breath on the palm of your hand. You must feel each breath. Do 52 Breaths.

8

8. Place one hand on top of the other in the center of your chest, with both thumbs pointing up toward your head. Pretend to feel bad, guilty, and sad. Bend your torso down to touch your head to each knee alternately. Touch each knee 11 times.

When you are very sad and very down, do this exercise and you will be surprised that you ever felt sad. This is how the body can switch the tendency. Activity carries the mind and spirit with it. And just to properly transfer the activity, that's what it takes.

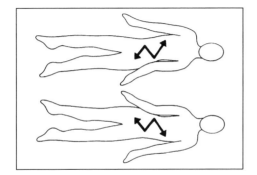

9

9. Lie down on your back and adjust your spine by moving your hips and rib cage in opposite directions in equal proportions, like a snake moving across a field. Give the vertebrae and nervous system a chance to be adjusted. Your hands and head remain on the floor. 3 Minutes.

10. Relax on your back and put yourself into a self-hypnotic sleep. 10 Minutes. Listen to Singh Kaur's *Rakhe Rakhan Har* tape.

To finish: Inhale and slowly wake yourself up. Roll your hands and feet. Do Cat stretch and the slowly get up.

"Are we mentally rich? If we are spiritually strong, we can do the impossible as possible. Is our discipline that strong?"

YB

36

January 24, 1996

1 & 2

3

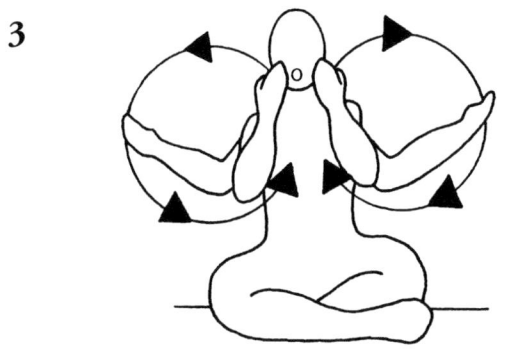

4

1. Sit in Easy Pose with a straight spine. Your left elbow is bent and rests close to the rib cage. The left palm faces upward, with the fingers pointing straight ahead. Make an "O" of your mouth and breathe through your mouth in the following manner. Inhale in three strokes as you touch the floor by your right side with the palm of your right hand and bring your right hand back toward your left palm. As the right palm touches the left palm, exhale in one stroke through the mouth. Time the motion of your right hand so you touch the floor and return within the three strokes of your inhale. You exhale in one stroke only as the right palm touches the left palm. Continue is this manner, breathing powerfully from the diaphragm. 4 Minutes.

2. Close your eyes and continue exercise #1, but move faster. This exercise can give you totally new nerves and stamina. It will break up blockages in the lungs. It can relax the body, take away muscle fatigue, and make you steady. 3 1/2 Minutes.

3. Inhale and exhale through the "O"-shaped mouth as you begin moving your arms in outward circles in front of your chest. The motion is something like scooping water up out of your lap, dashing it on your face, and circling your arms back to your lap. Move vigorously to open up your chest and to exercise the muscles of your shoulder blades. 3 1/2 Minutes.

4. Rest your right hand on your left at the center of your chest about level with your shoulders. The palms face down. Keep the hands touching as you move them four to six inches up and down. Move rapidly. Breathe through the "O"-shaped mouth in time with the movement. 1 1/2 Minutes. This exercise sends new serum to the brain and can help relieve depression.

"We live by the beat of the heart, not by the thoughts of the head... Man who lives by the beat of the heart, continuously meditating on the name of God, shall find heavens here and hereafter."

YB

5

6

7

5. Stand up and dance, shaking the entire body to the rhythmic beat of Bangara music. Lift your arms in the air, loosen your shoulders, spine, and hips. Break up your body blocks with rhythmic movement. Move vigorously and make yourself sweat. This is good for your circulation. 11 Minutes. After opening the diaphragm in the preceding exercises, this dance process is necessary.

6. Spread your legs shoulder width apart, keeping your knees straight. Lean over so that your torso is parallel with the ground. Rest your hands on your knees to support your torso. Let your lower back stretch out, allow it to open up. 1 Minute. Move directly into the next position.

7. Stay in the same position, but relax your arms and allow your body to hang forward. Bounce slowly and gently, allowing the weight of your body to stretch the spine and the muscles in the back of the legs. 30 Seconds. Inhale and gently rise up straight.

    To finish: move in a relaxed and relaxing manner from one position to the other in the following manner. Inhale as you relax forward. Exhale as your rise up straight. Continue inhaling forward and exhaling as you straighten up four more times.

    If a person's shoulders get tight, that person feels old and lifeless. You cannot be sick if you neither allow crystals to form in your feet nor allow your shoulders to get tight.

5-28-84

1. Come into Cow Pose on your hands and knees. Balancing on both hands and your left knee, extend your right leg straight back and then return to the starting position. Then extend your left leg straight back and return to the starting position. Continue alternately moving your legs, making sure that the extended leg is parallel to the ground, not angled up or down. 1 1/2 Minutes. Coordinate the leg movement with a powerful navel breath and continue for an additional 1 1/2 Minutes. With each pull, breathe in and breathe out. There is no need of a quick breath.

1 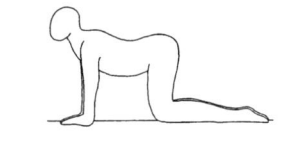 **2**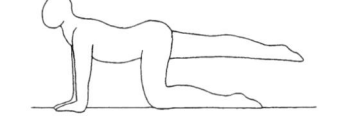

2. Remain in Cow Pose. Repeat the movement of exercise #1, but as each leg is extended straight backward, touch your forehead to the floor and then return to the starting position. Continue extending alternate legs and bowing for 3 1/2 Minutes coordinating the movement with a powerful navel breath.

3  **4**   **5**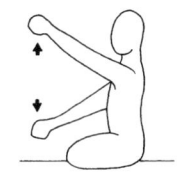

3. Remain in Cow Pose. Repeat the movement of exercise #2, but extend each leg up at an angle so that your whole body slants at a 60 degree angle when your forehead touches the floor. Continue alternately extending the legs up at an angle while bowing for 4 Minutes. Keep your knees straight. This exercise refreshes the blood supply to the brain.

4. Sit in Easy Pose and interlock your hands behind your back, keeping your elbows straight but not locked. Bend forward, touch your forehead to the floor, raising your arms as high as you can in Yoga Mudra. Return to the starting position. Inhale through your nose as you bend forward. Exhale powerfully through your mouth, like a lion, as you rise up. 2 1/2 Minutes.

5. Sit in Easy Pose with your arms held straight out in front, parallel to the ground. With the palms facing down, make your hands into fists, thumbs inside. Move your left arm up to 45 degrees as your right arm moves down to 45 degrees. Then move your right arm up to 45 degrees as your left arm moves down to 45 degrees. No bend in the elbows. Continue this alternate arm movement with Breath of Fire. Really move your navel. 2 Minutes.

6 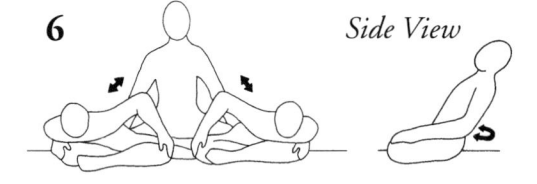 *Side View*

6. Sit in Easy Pose with your hands resting on your knees. Lean back and rotate your lower back and hips in a backward arc to the left side. As your left hipbone comes over your left thigh, lean forward to bring your left shoulder to your left knee, with your spine stretched straight, keeping your neck in necklock. Then reverse the motion, rotating your lower back and hips in a backward

arc to the right side. As your right hipbone comes over your right thigh, lean forward to bring your right shoulder to your right knee, with your spine stretched straight, keeping your neck in necklock. Continue to rotate to each side, loosening up the sacrum area and stretching the sides of the hips. 2 Minutes.

7

7. Stand up with your arms straight up above your head. Bend forward 90 degrees so that your upper body and arms form a straight line and are parallel to the ground. Remain in this position without moving for 2 Minutes.
Still in this position, try to become emotional and release this emotion by yelling, groaning, and making noise. 2 Minutes.

8

8. Still standing, bend forward until your hands touch the floor. Walk in place, first lifting the left hand and the right foot up from the floor and then lifting the right hand and the left foot up from the floor. Continue. Move rhythmically and briskly. 6 1/2 Minutes.

9

9. Sit in Easy Pose. Swing your arms to the left side and up 60 degrees. Then swing them to the right side and up 60 degrees. The palms face downward and both arms are parallel to each other as they move. Both arms move together. Swing the arms freely from the shoulders, but keep your elbows straight and your arms stiff. Use the weight of your arms to add force to your movement. 2 Minutes.

10. Sit in Crow Pose and jump up and down as high as you can. 45 Seconds. Continue jumping and breathe out through your mouth with the sound "HA" as you jump. 45 Seconds. "Be sure to do this exercise with your weight balanced on both sides. Jump only to the capacity and strength of your knees and legs." GCSK

10

11. Sit in Easy Pose with your palms together in front of your face, thumbs even with your nose and three to four inches in front of it. Your elbows are out to the sides and angling slightly downward. Close your eyes and chant "Har, Har, Har, Har, Haree Nam" in a monotone. (One repetition of the mantra takes about 3 seconds). 4 Minutes.

12. Lie down on your back and breathe deeply and heavily through your mouth. Between the navel and mouth, project out through the breath. 6 Minutes. In class, Yogi Bhajan played the gong during this meditation.

11

To finish: While lying on your back, begin to roll your neck in circles. Slowly and gradually rise up, still rolling your neck in circles, rising up inch by inch. 30 Seconds. When you are sitting up, begin to move your whole body. 10 Seconds. Finally, raise your hands in the air and shake them vigorously. 20 Seconds.

*"If we are not spiritually strong, then we can't negotiate properly.
If we are not mentally strong, then we do not have the grit to continue to negotiate.
Then we build more guns and bombs."*

YB

40

Achieve an Experience of God

August 22, 1986

Sit in Easy Pose, bend your elbows so that your upper arms are by your rib cage, and the hands are at shoulder level, palms facing forward. Bring each hand into Surya Mudra with the thumb and sun finger (ring finger) touching. Keep the other three fingers straight. Silently meditate to *Rahke Rakhan Har* by Singh Kaur. Your hands are in Surya Mudra and you are meditating to a Surya Shabd. Close your eyes and go through your oneness. Let the surya or sun energy circulate. Start with 11 minutes and work up to 31 Minutes.

"There is no God outside you. Neither was, nor is, nor shall be. It is all in you. The very breath of life is Divine."

YB

Become Calm
Earth to Self

January 31, 1996

Extend your Jupiter (index) fingers on both hands. Lock the other fingers down with your thumbs. Time your movements with the tape *Sat Nam Wahe Guru #2* by Jagjit Singh. Close your eyes and concentrate on the movement.

Touch your Jupiter fingers to the floor on either side of you when the ragi chants "Sat ."

Touch your Jupiter fingers together in front of your chin when the ragi chants "Nam."

Touch your Jupiter fingers to the floor on "Sat ."

Touch your Jupiter fingers in front of your chin on "Nam.

Touch your Jupiter fingers to the floor on "Wah-hay."

Touch your Jupiter fingers in front of your chin on "Guroo."

Touch your Jupiter fingers to the floor on "Wah-hay ."

Touch your Jupiter fingers in front of your chin on "Guroo."

Continue for 3 Minutes.

When you are very tense, please do this and you will become calm, quiet, peaceful, and tranquil. If you get a headache doing this exercise, it may mean that you have poor circulation. If you miss when you try to touch your fingers, it means you are not concentrating.

"Yoga is a science of reality and an experiential proof of the sacredness of all life."

YB

42

Become Intuitive

March 9, 1998

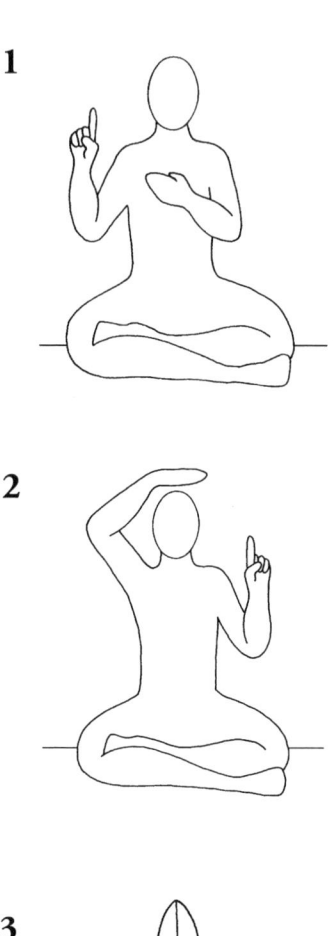

These exercises gently work on the pituitary. They are to recharge and enrich your energy and to counteract frustration, depression, and computer sicknesses.

1. Place your left hand over your heart center. Bend the right elbow, point the Jupiter (index) finger upward, with the thumb locking down the other three fingers. Consciously keep the spine very straight and pulled up, with no weight on the buttocks. The eyes are closed. Inhale slowly and deeply through the nose, hold your breath, and then exhale slowly with a whistle through the mouth. Imagine that something very pure and divine in you is calling. Reach out and make contact with your own Infinity. Create a feeling of being exalted by your own self. 7 Minutes. Inhale deeply and shift position.

2. Put your right hand either slightly above or just touching your head. Bend the left elbow, point the Jupiter (index) finger of the left hand upward and lock down the other three fingers with the thumb. Keep the spine pulled up straight. This is very important for the grey matter of the brain. Close your eyes and continue the same breath as in exercise one. 4 Minutes.

3. Lock your hands in Prayer mudra with your fingers up straight. Stretch your arms over your head. Keep your spine straight and stretch up from the armpits. Continue the same breath. You are consciously re-circulating your energy to give your body new life.
2 1/2 Minutes.

4

5

6

4. Put your right hand over your left at the center of your chest. Sit and deeply relax. Meditate to Singh Kaur's *Rakhe Rakhan Har* tape. Listen, relax, breathe, and be. 3 1/2 Minutes.

5. Inhale deeply and press your hands against your navel point. Chant along with Simran Kaur's *Tantric Har* tape. Each time you chant "Har," press the navel forcefully with your hands. The eyes are closed. 3 Minutes.

6. To finish: come into elbow lock position. The elbows are bent, with each hand grasping the the upper arm slightly above the opposite elbow. The arms are held parallel to the ground at shoulder height. Inhale, hold your breath 5-10 seconds, squeeze the spine, and tighten all the muscles of the body. Exhale. Repeat this sequence two more times.

"Meditation is not for anything but to become intuitive. It is not emotional, it is not sentimental, it is not attached. It is a basic reality of life."

YB

January 31, 1996

Sit in easy pose with your chin in and your chest out. Stick your tongue all the way out and keep it out as you rapidly breathe in and out through your mouth. This is called Dog Breath. Continue this panting diaphragm breath for 3-5 Minutes.

To finish: inhale, hold your breath 15 seconds, press the tongue hard against the upper palate. Exhale. Repeat this sequence two more times.

This exercise brings energy to your immune system to fight infection. It is a very healing exercise. When you feel a tingling in your toes, thighs, and lower back it is an indication that you are doing the exercise correctly.

"If the food you eat makes your mind go berserk and your body is churned in pain, that food is worthless."

Guru Nanak

Conquer Inner Anger and Burn It Out

March 8, 1999

Sit in easy pose with your arms stretched out straight to the sides. There is no bend in the elbows. The Jupiter (Index) finger points upward and the thumb locks down the other fingers. The power of Jupiter, the knowledge, should be tough, stiff, and straight.

Close your eyes and concentrate on your spine. Inhale deeply through the rolled tongue (Sitali breath) and exhale through the nose. 11 Minutes.

To finish: Inhale deeply, hold the breath for 10 seconds while you stretch your arms out to the sides as far as possible, exhale. Repeat this sequence two more times.

This meditation can be done either in the morning or the evening. If you do this eleven minutes every day, your entire life will change. This will give you a new life. Do this for forty days, it will change your personality from A to Z.

"Taking is suffering. Giving is happiness."

YB

46

February 2, 1976

1

1. Sit calmly in a comfortable position. Relax your arms at your sides with your palms facing forward. Alternately bend each elbow bringing your palms toward the center of your chest, but do not touch your chest. Do not bend the wrists or hands. Move as rapidly as you can, you should have sweat on your forehead after a couple of minutes. Maintain a balance in the rhythmic motion of your hands. If your hands hit each other, it means that this balance is upset.

This exercise clears out the lymph glands in the upper chest, makes the heart healthy, and is good for the breast area. It works on the left and right hemispheres of the brain, creating a balance bewteen them. It will make you quick to know what to do.

As a warm-up for the following meditation, practice this exercise for 3 to 11 Minutes. (If you wish to practice this exercise on its own, do it for 10 or 15 minutes every morning.)

"Fact is, nobody can control any-body. All you can do is flow with each other like rivers and streams flow with each other and end up in the same ocean. All things come from God and all things go to God."

YB

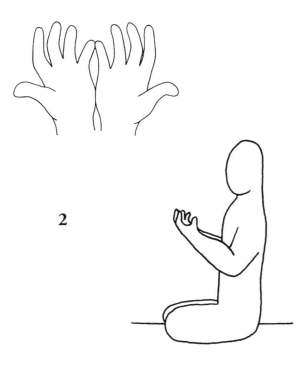

2

2. Immediately after practicing the warm-up, with your elbows still at your sides, bring your forearms up to sixty degrees. Place the sides of the hands together, palms up, at the height of the diaphragm. The fingers are relaxed and spread slightly. The thumbs are relaxed and slightly up and out.

Look right into the center of the hands, where the Mercury (pinky) fingers are. Inhale deeply and chant "Hariang" eight times on one breath. Each chanting cycle takes about ten seconds.

There are eighty-four points in the upper part of the mouth and the touch of the tongue works like acupressure. When you speak, this tongue touches those areas and stimulates the nervous system and brain. The words we call mantra are designed to stimulate a particular combination of meridians in the mouth. These words also have a projective power. The theory is that the huge computer mind is infinite and our mind is limited. If you know the combination of the frequency of the signal which can tap the resources of the Infinite Mind, then the flow of Infinity will start appearing to your finite mind. Mantra is nothing but a telecommunication of the finite unto the Infinite. The individual creates a frequency of vibration within his electro-magnetic field to tap the electro-magnetic field of the Universe.

"Hariang" means "Shiva, Destroyer of Evil". It is a powerful mantra which brings wealth and intuitive opportunity. When chanting "Hariang" the tip of the tongue touches the roof of the mouth, behind the front teeth to make the "r" sound.

It may take a couple of months to bring this meditation under your control, But, if you do this meditation for ninety days, it will activate your brain so that you will know exactly what is what. It will make you super sensitive. It will make it intuitively possible for you to live creatively to your own potential and to tap the opportunities around you.

January 31, 1996

Sit in easy pose with your elbows bent , palms facing each other about shoulder height. Touch the tip of the Mercury (pinkie) finger to the tip of the thumb. Keep the other three fingers straight so that your Sun, Saturn, and Jupiter antennae are lined up. Stick your tongue all the way out and breathe in and out through your mouth as fast as you can. This panting diaphragm breath is called Dog Breath. Close your eyes and listen to the breath. The sound of this breath is "Har." 10 Minutes.

To finish: Inhale deeply, roll your tongue inward, and hold your breath for 15 seconds. Exhale. Repeat this sequence two more times.

This kriya unlocks the diaphragm, takes away anger, and can return you to the innocent state of childhood.

"Try to live innocent, straight, calm, quiet, and peaceful."

YB

Excel and Build Your Healing Force

August 22, 1986

When you want to excel despite all deficiencies, do the following kriya.

Sit in Easy Pose with your spine straight. Interlock your fingers and raise your hands over your head, so that your arms become a halo around it. Make the halo as round as you can, neither up too high nor so low that it touches your head. Concentrate at your navel and meditate to Jasbir Kaur's *Mul Mantra* tape.
11-31 Minutes.

This meditation uses the physical flow of your energy to activate the body's healing force. Practice it for 31 minutes a day for fifteen days and see the results in your physical well-being.

"You'll never know who you are, if you have not disciplined yourself to know who you are."

YB

50

2-21-97

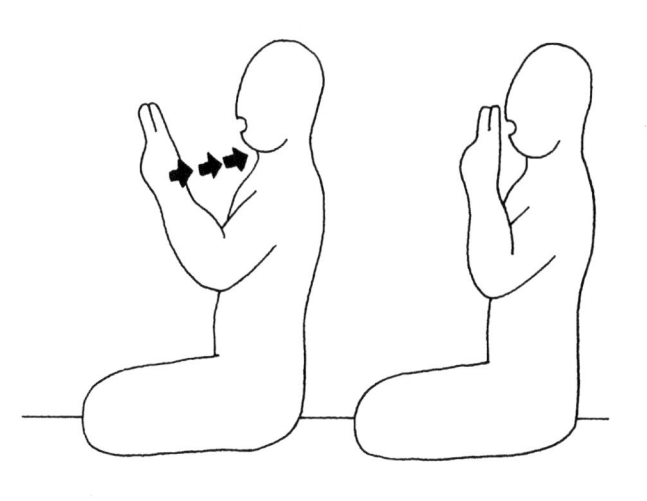

Sit in Easy Pose. Put each hand in this mudra: lock down the Mercury (pinky) finger and Sun (ring) finger with the thumb and keep the Jupiter and Saturn fingers (index and middle fingers) together and pointing straight up.

The elbows are bent and rest against the rib cage. Your hands are at shoulder level about twelve inches from the body. The palms of the hands are facing each other and stay facing each other throughout the movement.

Inhale in three or four quick strokes through the "O" shaped mouth. With each stroke of the breath, jerk the hands back toward your shoulders. Both hands move at the same time.

The inhale portion, during which you jerk your hands back three or four times, is extremely fast. It should be completed in about one second.

Exhale through the mouth in one stroke and return to the starting position. This jerky motion is a self-created nervousness done consciously so that the energy in you can balance. Continue for 11 Minutes

To finish: Inhale, hold the breath for 10-15 seconds, stay in the position, and repeat the jerking movement of the hands so powerfully that the whole body shakes. Move your spine, shoulders, and arms with your shaking. Repeat this sequence two more times.

After the first two minutes of this kriya the action becomes difficult, but you must continue to move quickly. This jerk can give you a new nervous system. When you become tired, it is the time to overcome the urge to slow down. Keep the rhythm and fight it out.

When practiced regularly and correctly, this kriya can give you a new nervous system. The nerves that have disconnected themselves and are dead will start connecting and finding a pathway. That's the power of the breath, the whole system will be shaking.

"The strength behind the muscles is the nerves. The strength behind the nerves is the stamina and the strength behind the stamina is you."

YB

For the Tattwas, Pranic Rib Cage, and Nervous System

May 30, 1996

1

1. Sit in Easy Pose with your spine straight. Keep your chin in and your chest out. Bend your elbows and support them on your rib cage with your palms facing toward your body. Allow the wrists to bend so the palms face upward, hands in front of the shoulders. Close your hands into fists and open them again rapidly and continuously. Put strength in your movement. 3 Minutes.

This creates an elementary balance which is one of the most beautiful and powerful things of the human body. It will stimulate the basic tattwas...Your breath will change. The pranic energy in the combination of your breath will change. You cannot buy that in the market, you have to produce it.

2

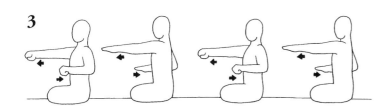

2. Still in easy pose, move your arms and shoulders like a bird in flight. Move fast. This balances both parts of the brain. Be sure that your shoulders move up and down with the movement of your arms. 3 minutes.

This adjusts the ribs, is beneficial to the heart, and improves circulation in the chest area. This will help to adjust the ribs and balance both sides of the brain. However, if you start to feel nauseated, stop immediately.

3

3. Sit in easy pose and look straight ahead. Reach forward with your right arm and, at the end of your forward movement, make your right hand into a fist. Pull your right arm back to your side as you reach forward with your left arm. At the end of the left arm's forward movement, the left hand is open with the fingers slightly spread. Move quickly and powerfully, reaching forward with alternate arms. 3 minutes. This is for the nervous system. Move very fast so that the breath changes.

(When Yogi Bhajan demonstrated this movement he made a fist of his right hand at the end of its forward reach. When his right hand returned to his side, it relaxed open with the fingers slightly spread. When he reached forward with his left arm, the left hand remained open. When his left hand returned to his side, he made it into a fist. The movement was timed so that extending arm reached its maximum forward extension at the same time that the retracting arm reached its resting point at his side.)

4

4. Bend your elbows with your palms facing forward, fingers slightly spread. Lean back 15 degrees. Close your eyes. Sit with your chin in and chest out. Balance your body from the chin, which is the moon center. Sing along with the tape "Meditation" by Wahe Guru Kaur and go into deep meditation. 15 minutes. The angle of the spine is important. If this exercise is done correctly, the basic psyche will change.

To finish: Inhale, lean back a little farther and stretch your spine vertebra by vertebra as you hold the breath 10-15 seconds. Repeat this sequence two more times.

Exercise one is for the tattwas, exercise two is for the pranic rib cage, and exercise three is for the nervous system.

"When you walk on the path of spirituality, one thing is very essential: you must see the Hand of God."

YB

1

1. Sit calmly in a comfortable position. Relax your arms at your sides with your palms facing forward. Alternately bend each elbow bringing your palms toward the center of your chest, but do not touch your chest. Do not bend the wrists or hands. Move as rapidly as you can, you should have sweat on your forehead after a couple of minutes. Maintain a balance in the rhythmic motion of your hands. If your hands hit each other, it means that this balance is upset.

"Richness is having the power of wealth. Prosperity is when you are purposefully satisfied."

YB

This exercise clears out the lymph glands in the upper chest, makes the heart healthy, and is good for the breast area. It works on the left and right hemispheres of the brain, creating a balance between them. It will make you quick to know what to do.

As a warm-up for the following meditation, practice this exercise for 3 to 11 Minutes. (If you wish to practise this exercise on its own, do it for 10 or 15 minutes every morning.)

2

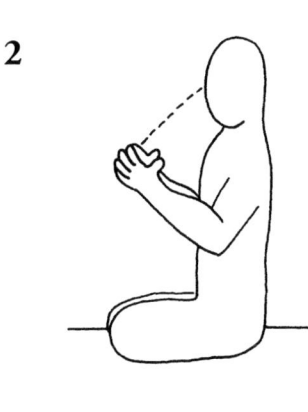

2. Still in the same position, loosely connect the fingertips to equalize the energy, leaving the thumbs separate and extended. The fingers are loosely separated and the hands are relaxed. ("Hariang" is not a neutral mantra so the thumbs which represent the ego, must be apart.) Look down sixty degrees through your hands. Chant "Hariang" sixteen times on each breath. (Each chanting cycle takes about 13-15 seconds.) 11-31 Minutes.

"Hariang" means "Shiva, Destroyer of Evil". It is a powerful mantra which brings wealth and intuitive opportunity. When chanting "Hariang" the tip of the tongue touches the roof of the mouth, behind the front teeth to make the "r" sound.

It may take a couple of months to bring this meditation under your control, but, if you do this meditation for ninety days, it will activate your brain so that you will know exactly what is what. It will make you super sensitive. It will make it intuitively possible for you to live creatively to your own potential and to tap the opportunities around you.

Hast Kriya
Earth to Heavens

January 31, 1996

Extend your Jupiter (index) fingers on both hands. Lock the other fingers down with your thumbs. Time your movements with the tape *Sat Nam Wahe Guru #2* by Jagjit Singh.
Touch your Jupiter fingers to the floor on either side of you when the ragi chants "Sat."
Touch your Jupiter fingers together over the top of your head when the ragi chants "Nam."
Touch your Jupiter fingers to the floor on either side of you when the ragi chants "Sat."
Touch your Jupiter fingers together over the top of your head when the ragi chants "Nam."
Touch your Jupiter fingers to the floor on either side of you when the ragi chants "Wah-hay."
Touch your Jupiter fingers together over the top of your head when the ragi chants "Guroo."
Touch your Jupiter fingers to the floor on either side of you when the ragi chants "Wah-hay."
Touch your Jupiter fingers together over the top of your head when the ragi chants "Guroo."

This kriya renews the nervous system and can heal nerve pain and sciatica. It is so powerful it can hold the Hand of God; so powerful, it can hold the hand of death. "Sat Nam Wahe Guru" is a Jupiter mantra.

The most graceful power and knowledge comes from Jupiter. Jupiter controls the medulla oblongata, the neurological center of the brain, and the three rings of the brain stem.

If you do this kriya for 22 minutes a day, you will totally change your personality. Power will descend from above and clean you out. Anger and obnoxiousness will disappear from your personality.

"We are all together in the One Creator's Consciousness."
YB

October 11, 1999

1 & 2

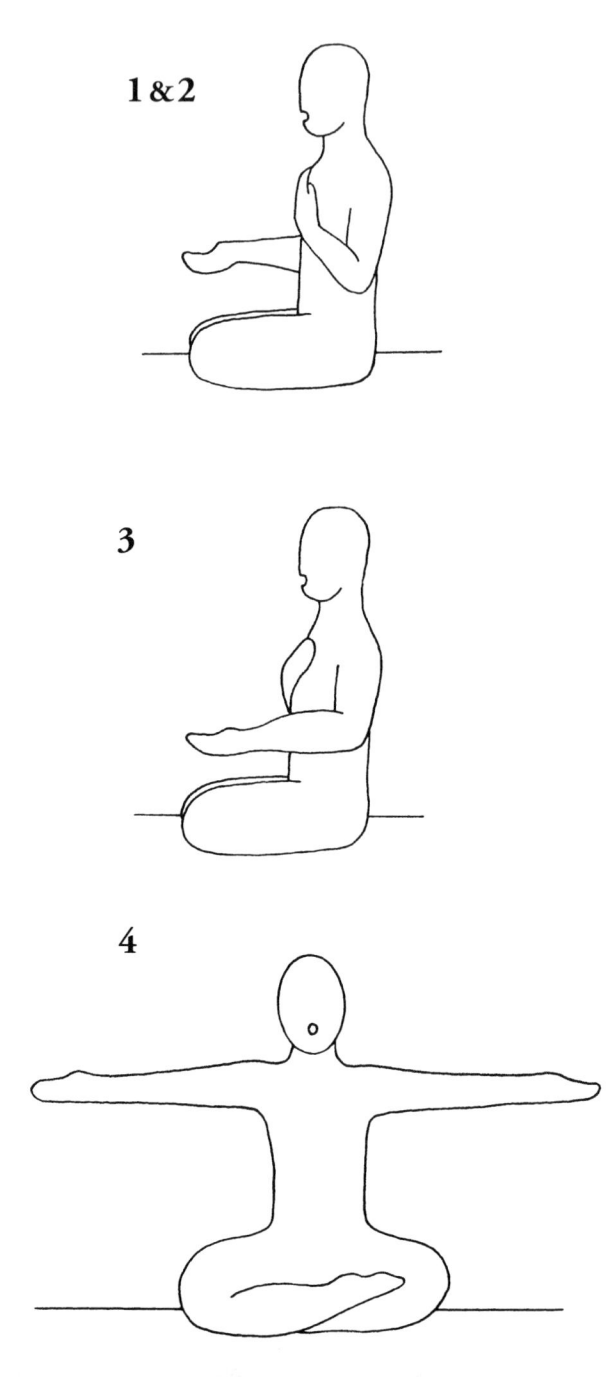

3

4

1. Sit in Easy Pose, with your left hand on your heart. The upper portion of your right arm is at your side, next to the ribs. The elbow is bent and the forearm extends forward, parallel to the floor. Your right palm faces upward and is cupped as if to receive water. Inhale deeply through the "O" shaped mouth, as if drinking the air. Exhale through the nose. Don't pull the air in , breathe it as if you are drinking it. This exercise will stimulate your immune system and your heart muscle. 22 Minutes.

2. Stay in the position and use your navel point to create a powerful Breath of Fire through the "O" mouth. 2 Minutes.

3. Change the hand position, the right hand is on your heart and the left arm extends forward with the hand cupped. Continue Breath of Fire through the "O" mouth for 2 1/2 Minutes. When you change the hand position, you will notice the difference.

4. Stretch your arms out to the sides, elbows straight, palms up. Continue Breath of Fire through the mouth.
2 Minutes.

5. To Finish: Inhale, hold the position, hold the breath 10-15 seconds as you stretch the spine up straight. Exhale. Repeat this sequence one more time, stretching the spine up.The last time inhale, hold the breath 15 seconds, and stretch the extended arms out to the sides as far as you can. Exhale and relax.

"You do not understand discipline. Discipline is the only friend, other than God, that you have."
YB

Magnificent Mantra

July, 1996

Sit in easy pose with your spine straight. Bend your elbows so that your hands are comfortably in front of you at approximately shoulder height. Chant the mantra:

Har Har Har Har Gobinday	God the Sustainer
Har Har Har Har Mukhanday	God the Liberator
Har Har Har Har Udaray	God the Enlightener
Har Har Har Har Aparay	God the Infinite
Har Har Har Har Hariang	God the Destroyer of Evil
Har Har Har Har Kariang	God the Creator
Har Har Har Har Nirnamay	God the Nameless
Har Har Har Har Akamay	God the Desireless

Each time you chant "Har," quickly open and close your hands as you pull the navel point in and up. Repeat these actions each time you chant "Har".
11 Minutes or 31 Minutes.

Consciously use your tongue to create the sounds. Pronounce the "a" in "Har" in the way you pronounce "u" in "hug". The "r" is produced in a special way using just the tip of the tongue to touch the roof of the mouth (just behind the front teeth) to make the "r" sound.

*"This mantra brings prosperity, happiness, and saves us from calamities.
It is a sound current which brings a shield and brings good luck and removes discomfort and disease.
It is the key to the doorway of self elevation."*

YB

56

June 17, 1994

1. Sit in Easy Pose with the fingers of your left hand in a vertical line touching the center of your forehead. Your right elbow is bent with the upper arm near the rib cage. The forearm and hand point upward. The right palm faces forward. Close your eyes and focus at the center of your chin, the moon center, through your closed eyes. Calm down, breathe slowly and concentrate at moon center. 11 Minutes.

After five minutes, if you concentrate correctly, fixing your eyes at your chin, the sushumna must start vibrating. Your forehead, where your hand is, will become hot. Then the body stops itching and hurting, and you can feel that you are successfully doing it. At six minutes it affects your nervous system. The ida and pingala will start going through commotions, but it is a positive sign.

2. In the same position, rhythmically chant "Har" with the tip of your tongue. (Chant at a rate of one "Har" per second.) 11 Minutes.

3. Remain in the same position. Inhale, hold your breath and stretch your spine upward. Hold your breath for as long as you can. (The goal is to hold your breath for one minute before exhaling.) Exhale like cannon fire through your mouth, inhale deeply, hold the breath and continue. 11 Minutes.
On the last inhale, look inward at your body. Send healing energy to those parts of your body that present themselves to your mind's eye at this time.

To finish: Inhale, hold your breath for 10 seconds, as you stretch your arms upward and shake out your hands. Repeat this sequence two more times. Relax.

This is a self-purifying meditation. It will give you a personality that is strong and pure, with a powerful projection. It purifies the sushumna, the divine nerve of you.

"Yoga was made for man to be healthy, happy, and holy. Kundalini Yoga was made for man to be healthy, happy, holy, and aware. Secret of your soul is awareness."

YB

Releasing Childhood Anger

March 9, 1999

Sit in easy pose with your arms stretched out straight to the sides. There is no bend in the elbows. Use your thumbs to lock down the Mercury and Sun fingers (pinkie and ring fingers) and extend the Jupiter and Saturn fingers (index and middle fingers). The palms face forward and the fingers point out to the sides.

Inhale deeply by sucking air through your closed teeth and exhale through your nose. 11 Minutes.

To finish: Inhale deeply, hold the breath for 10 seconds while you stretch your spine up and stretch your arms out to the sides, and exhale. Repeat this sequence two more times.

This meditation will give you some subtle powers. It will change you inside and out. It can be done either in the morning or the evening, but if you do it in the evening, the next morning you will find that your whole caliber and energy is changed.

"Show some respect for your hidden power. Awaken it!"

YB

58

Raa Maa Daa Saa Saa Say So Hung
Healing Meditation

December 20, 1999

Developing the power to heal:

Sit in Easy Pose. Put your left hand on your navel point. Your right arm is by your right side, elbow bent, with the palm facing forward. You are holding your right hand up as if you are taking an oath. This meditation is done with Gurnam's *RaMaDaSa, Healing Sounds* tape or CD. You may either chant out loud or meditate silently. The movement of the kriya is timed with the chanting of "Raa Maa Daa Saa Saa Say So Hung" by Gurnam.

At "Raa", slowly begin moving your right arm forward from the starting position and continue slowly moving so that your arm is straight out in front of you with the palm facing downward at "Hung." The movement begins with "Raa" and is completed at "Hung." Then the right arm moves back to the starting position by your side and the movement begins again at "Raa." The right arm moves as if giving a blessing. Start with 11 minutes and work up to 31 Minutes. Gradually, over time, you may increase the time to a maximum practice time of 2 1/2 Hours.

Yogi Bhajan said that this is a meditation to practice for the rest of your life. It is a simple exercise that can give you the power to heal.

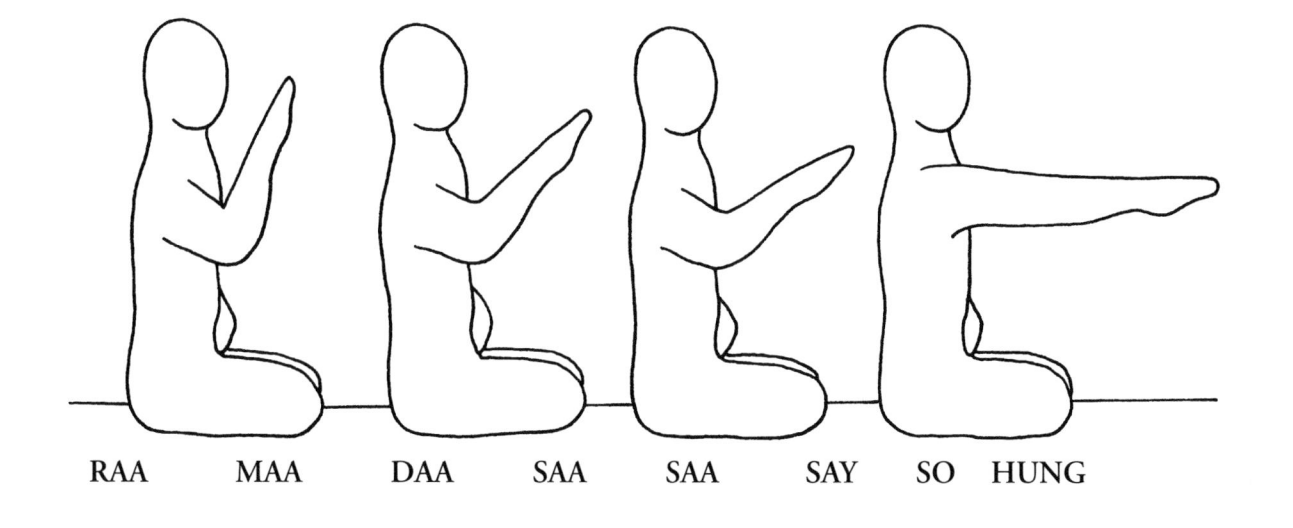

RAA   MAA   DAA   SAA   SAA   SAY   SO   HUNG

Variations for healing others:

1. You may do this kriya using your left hand to hold the hand of the person you want to heal. The right hand moves as described above. You may chant the mantra out loud or mentally and silently.

OR

2. If the person needing healing is very ill, shaking and shivering, you can place your left hand on their navel point and place your right hand on their pituitary. You may chant the mantra out loud or mentally and silently.

"People will be attracted to you like the magnet attracts iron. They will ask you for help. They are not asking "you" for help, they are asking your aura to help them. It is a different psyche...People will reach out to you because they will feel, in the presence of your arcline and aura, some calmness, some quietness where they might get to some rest. Just extend yourself...just help them to calm their inner volcano."

YB

August 22, 1986

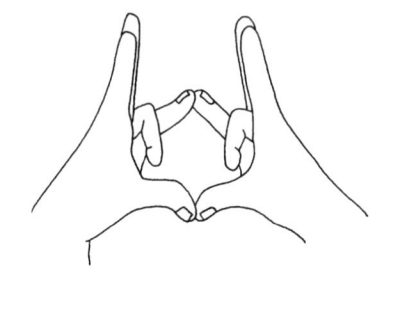

Sit in Easy Pose. Put the hands in the following mudra 3" to 4" in front of the center of the chest: touch the thumb and Mercury (pinky) finger of one hand to the thumb and Mercury finger of the other hand. Bend the Sun (ring) fingers in toward the palms, but do not let them touch the palms. Leave the Jupiter (index) and Saturn (middle) fingers pointing straight up, but not touching. Meditatively listen to "Beloved God," the first song on Singh Kaur's *Peace Lagoon* tape. Start with 11 minutes and work up to 31 Minutes.

This meditation activates the Mercury power, the power of communication.

"Teaching is to reach into another's soul. And, when the soul is lit, the God prevails."

YB

December 20, 1999

Sit in Easy Pose. Put the fingers of your left hand on your forehead touching your third eye point. Extend your right arm out straight forward from your shoulder with the palm facing left. Close your eyes, hold the position, breathe slowly and deeply, and meditate silently. Recharge your body with energy. 18 Minutes.

To finish: Inhale, hold your breath 5-10 seconds, and exhale. Repeat this sequence one more time. Then inhale, hold your breath 10-15 seconds,and, with your fingers interlocked over your head, stretch your spine upward. Exhale and relax.

This kriya is for handling the pressures of the Information Age. As you do the posture, your breathing will change. Use your breath, the energy of prana, to carry you through. Keep your right arm stretched out parallel to the ground, to catch up with the magnetic field of the earth. Your left hand is at your pituitary to balance the heavens. The force of your breath will become longer and more powerful. Your body will start feeling pain. This pain will give you endurance, endurance will cause you to rise above your situation, and, once you rise above yourself, you've got it.

"This life is not for wasting. It is for reaching to the wonderlands of your own consciousness."

YB

Surrounding Yourself With Protection
Chii-a* Kriya

February 24, 1997

Mudra

Sit in Easy Pose. Touch the tip of the thumb and the tip of the Jupiter finger (index finger). The other fingers are relaxed. With your hands in this mudra, close your eyes, and move your arms in the following sequence. Chant using the tip of your tongue.

1. Stretch your arms out to the sides with the palms facing forward. Keep your elbows straight. Chant "Har."

2. Without bringing your hands near your shoulders, move your hands directly in front of you with your palms down, elbows by your sides, and your forearms pointing straight out in front of your body. Chant "Haray."

3. Bring your hands up by your shoulders, palms facing out. Chant "Haree."

*Side View
posture #2 and #5*

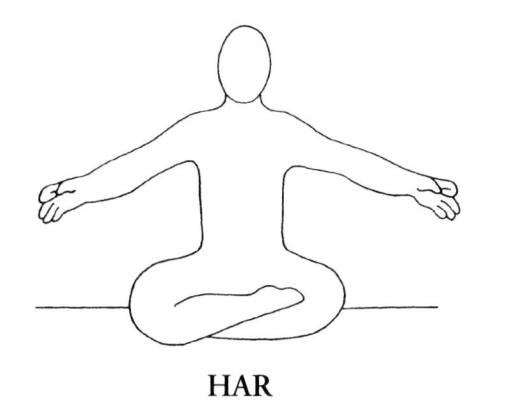

HAR

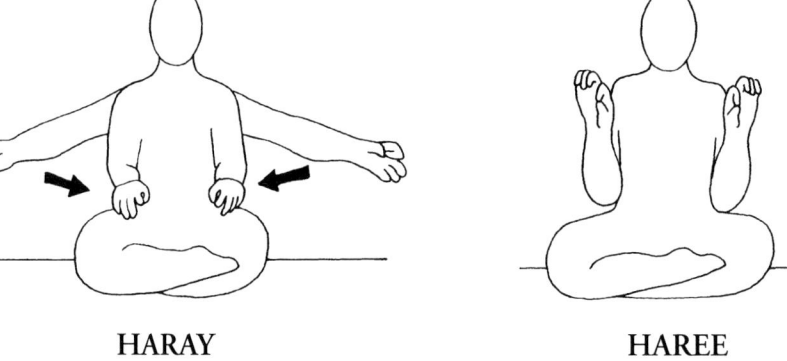

HARAY

HAREE

"The sound current has an Infinite power on God. It can bind God. It has the power. It is the only power which is given to the human to excel. Vaak Siddhi** is the perfection of the sound projection. Guru Nanak explained it, 'Through the mouth you utter a sound current, to which God listens with love.' What you talk is not a sound current. The sound current is that which you create with the organic matter of your body where you use your pranas and that has a projective power."

4. Stretch your arms out to the sides again. Chant "Wah."

5. Bring your arms directly to the front, palms down. Chant "Hay."

6. Bring your hands up near your shoulders. Chant "Guroo."

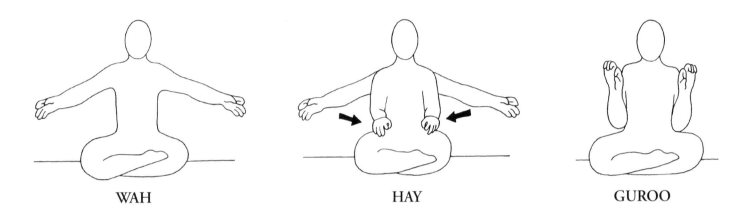

WAH   HAY   GUROO

Continue for 11 Minutes.

    To finish: Inhale, hold the breath 15-20 seconds, keep your arms in position #6 and squeeze your rib cage as you stretch your spine upward. Exhale. Repeat this sequence two more times.
    When in your life nothing works. There comes a moment in your life when nothing works. If all shelter and hope is gone. When the enemies overcome and friends have left. Do this
meditation: "Har, Haray, Haree, Wah-hay Guroo". It has six sounds, don't take it as a mantra, these are six unchangeable sounds. What surrounds you is six: the four directions and up and down. Meditate on these six in this way and they will cover you. It is not an obligation, it is a directive.

*Chii-a is the Gurmukhi word for "six". In this Kriya there are six unchangeable sounds which affect the six directions.
** Vaak siddhi is a spiritual power that what you say, happens.

64

November 17, 1991

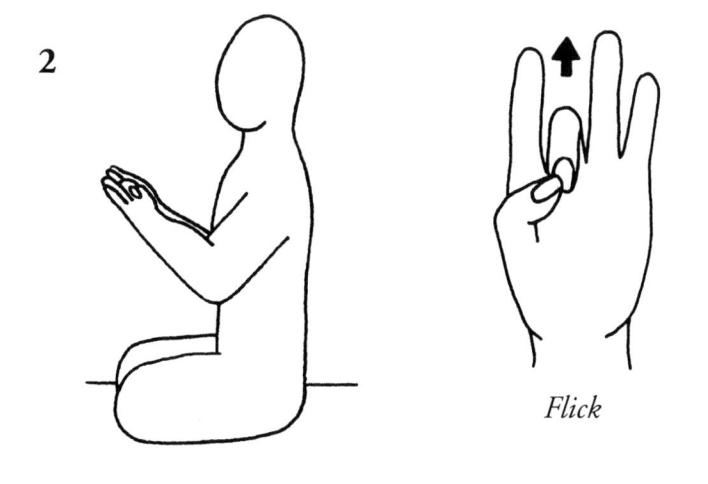

1

2

Flick

1. Pitta Kriya: Sit in Easy Pose. Put your left palm on the center of your chest. Bend your right elbow. Make a cup of your right hand. Move your cupped hand past your right ear, as if you are throwing water over your shoulder. Keep your right arm moving back and forth, making sure that the right wrist passes the right ear.
11 Minutes.
Inhale deeply and hold your breath for 20 seconds as you press your right arm as far back as possible, stretching the armpit. Exhale like cannon fire through the mouth. Repeat this sequence two more times.

This exercise works on the liver. The liver is "that by which you live," because it cleans the bloodstream of impurities. The bloodstream interacts with every cell of your body. When the bloodstream is polluted, it is very difficult to achieve a health-sustaining balance in your body chemistry.

In the eleven minutes of this exercise, the liver is stimulated to cleanse the blood and the glands are stimulated to secrete and improve the chemistry of the blood. This combination strenghtens your ability to handle stress more effectively.

2. Sit in Easy Pose. Focus your eyes at the tip of your nose. Bend your elbows and press them against your rib cage so that your forearms angle upward. With your palms facing up, hold down the first joint of each Saturn (middle) finger with the thumb. Flick both Saturn fingers at the same time as you chant "Har". Continue rapidly flicking the fingers and chanting, using the tip of your tongue to chant.
11 Minutes.
Inhale deeply, hold the breath 15-20 seconds, and continue to flick the Saturn fingers. Exhale and repeat this sequence two more times.

This exercise brings all the chakras into balance and balances the Saturn energy (the energy of purity and discipline) in your psyche.

"Stress takes you away from you all the time."

YB

3. Sit in Easy Pose. Focus your eyes at the tip of your nose. Extend both arms out to the sides, parallel to the floor, palms down. Allow no bend in the elbows. Criss-cross your arms in front of you, horizontally, over and under (alternating which arm crosses on top). Chant "Har" each time your arms cross. 11 Minutes. Inhale deeply, hold the breath for 5-10 seconds, and continue to criss-cross your arms. Exhale and repeat this sequence two more times.

It is said that all diseases come from a weak nervous system. In eleven minutes this exercise strenghtens and balances the parasympathetic and sympathetic nervous systems so that the action nervous system may correctly know what to do.

These fundamental kriyas shall never fail you if you do them for 11 minutes each. The practice time must be exact. These are not exercises that can be done for less than 11 minutes or for more than 11 minutes.

In the first exercise you balanced the glandular system, the second exercise balanced the chakras, and the last exercise balanced the three nervous systems. If all these systems support you, how can you be stressed?

3

Aap Sahaaee Hoa, Sachay Da, Sachaa Dhoaa, Har Har Har
The Lord Himself has become our protector.
The Truest of the True has taken care of us. God. God. God.

Akaal
Eternal, Undying God

Sat Naam
Truth is God's name

Wah hay Guroo
Great beyond description is the wisdom of God

Ek Ong Kar Sat Naam Siree Wah hay Guroo
There is one Creator, who created this creation.
Truth is His name. Great beyond description is the wisdom of God.

Dhan Dhan Ram Das Gur
Dhan Dhan Raam Daas Gur, jin siria tineh savaariaa
Poore hoee karamaat, aap sireejana-haaray dhaariaa
Sikhee ateh sangatee, paarabrahm kar namaskaariaa
Atal ataao atol too,tayraa ant na paaravaariaa
Jinee too sayviaa bhao kar, say tudh paar utaaria
Labh lobh kaam krodh moho, maar kadhe tudh sapaaravaariaa
Dhan so tayraa taan heh, sach tayraa pehsakaariaa
Nanak too(n) lehenaa too(n) heh, Gur Amar too veecharria
Guru ditta taa man saadhaariaa

Blessed, blessed is Guru Ram Das
The Lord who created Thee, He alone has adorned Thee
Complete is Thy miracle
The Creator Himself has installed Thee on the throne.
Deeming Thee as the Transcendent Lord, Thine followers and congregations bow before Thee.
Thou art immovable, unfathomable, and immeasurable.
Thou hast no end or bounds.
They who serve Thee with love,
Them Thou ferriest across.
Avarice, covetousness, sexual desire, wrath and worldly love,
Thou hast beaten and driven out with all their ramifications.
Praiseworthy is Thy place
True are Thine bounties.
Thou art Nanak, Thou art Angad
Thou art Guru Amar Das, so do I deem Thee.
When I saw the Guru, then was my soul sustained.

Chattr Chakkr Vartee
Jaap Sahib: The Last Four Lines

Chattr chakkr vartee, chattr chakkr bhugatay
Suyumbhav subhang, sarab daa sarab jugatay
Dukaalang pranaasee, dayaalang saroopay
Sadaa ang sangay, abhangang bibhootay.

Thou art pervading in all the four quarters of the universe,
Thou are the enjoyer in all the four quarters of the universe.
Thou art self-illumined and united with all.
Destroyer of bad times, embodiment of mercy.
Thou art ever within us.
Thou art the everlasting giver of undestroyable power.

On the pronunciation of the mantra "Har"

    The"a" in the mantra "Har" is pronounced like the "u" in "hug". The "r" is produced in a special way with just the tip of the tongue touching the roof of the mouth, behind the front teeth, to make the "r" sound.

    The mantra is chanted by pulling the navel in strongly and, as the air is forced from the lungs, the sound "Har" flows out with the breath, ending as the tip of the tongue touches the roof of the mouth.

Har
God

Har Har, Wah-hay Guru
God, God. Great beyond description is the wisdom of God

Har Har Haree, Har Har Haree
God, God, the Merged One
God, God, the Merged One

Har, Har, Har, Har, Haree Naam
God, God, God, God, God's Name

Haree Har, Haree Har, Haree Har Haree
Creative God, the power of God
Creative God, the power of God
Creative God, the power of God Creating

Hariang
Shiva, Destroyer of evil

Rakhe Rakhan Har
Rakhay Rakhanahaar aap ubaarian
Gur ke pairee paa-ay kaaj savaarian
Hoa aap dayaal manaho naa(n) visaari-an
Saadh janaa kai sang bhavjal taarian
Saakat nindak dusht khin maaeh bidaarian
Tis saahib kee tayk Naanak manai maaeh
Jis simrat sukh hoay sagalay dookh jaaeh.

Oh, God. You save us all and take us across, uplifting and giving excellence.
You gave us the touch of the lotus feet of the Guru, and all our jobs are done with perfection.
You have become merciful, kind, and compassionate; and so our mind does not forget You.
In the company of the holy, you take us from misfortune and calamities, scandals, and disrepute.
That great Lord is my anchor. Nanak keep Him firmly in my mind.
By meditating and repeating His Name, all happiness comes and all sorrows and pain go away.

Raa Maa Daa Saa, Saa Say So Hung
Sun, Moon, Earth, Infinity.
Infinity, Infinity, I am Thou.

Music can be purchased from your local yoga center or the following:

Spirit Voyage
spiritvoyage.com
888-735-4800

Ancient Healing Ways
Store.a-healing.com
877-853-5351

70

Resources

The Kundalini Research Institute: Your Source for
Kundalini Yoga as Taught by Yogi Bhajan®
Teacher Training, Online Resources, Publishing, and Research

www.kriteachings.org

The Yogi Bhajan Library of Teachings
Keeping the Legacy Alive! Donate Today!

www.kriteachings.org

For information regarding international events:

www.3HO.org

To find a teacher in your area or for more information
about becoming a Kundalini Yoga teacher:

www.kundaliniyoga.com

Of further interest:

www.sikhnet.org

Kundalini Yoga as taught by Yogi Bhajan®

Kundalini Research Institute